5.30 A.M. WITHOUT WARNING

5.30 A.M. WITHOUT WARNING

Jakki Sidney

Book Guild Publishing
Sussex, England

First published in Great Britain in 2012 by
The Book Guild Ltd
Pavilion View
19 New Road
Brighton, BN1 1UF

Typesetting in Garamond by
Nat-Type, Cheshire

Printed in Great Britain by
CPI Group (UK) Ltd, Croydon, CR0 4YY

A catalogue record for this book is available from
The British Library.

ISBN 978 1 84624 612 8

Acknowledgements

If we begin by thanking so many people, there will not be enough pages for the book! But, without acknowledging Carol, Mike and Paul's input by coming to our rescue in their own inimitable way from day one until the final chapter, this would have been a totally different story entitled *Misery and Misfortune.*

Friendship, support and kindness go a very long way and our heartfelt appreciation goes to great friends who supported us throughout the ordeal and to new friends who are very special to us.

I also want to thank Andrew Greene and a group of unique people from 'INNOCENT', who helped me just by being there.

Finally, and on a lighter note: as I am absolute rubbish at the complicated intricacies of computer technology, other than straightforward emails, correspondence and text messages on my mobile, I have to thank all the publishing team for their tenacity and immense patience whilst trying in vain to explain to me how to send my edited pages across by attachment. It was one big blur and I desperately missed snail mail.

1

How do you begin to write a book that isn't a fictitious gem of an inventive imagination belonging to the wonderful worlds of Frederick Forsyth or John Grisham? This is fact, it's not just a piece of storytelling; but whoever reads it will probably think it's impossible, even unbelievable, and give me extra credit for copying my heroes. Let me assure you, the sad reality is that it actually happened to my family; and if it can happen to us, it can happen to anyone! To quote a very famous English barrister QC: 'No one is safe; it can happen to you, you and you. If British justice is supposed to be the best in the world, God help the rest of the planet!'

As an accountant, my husband isn't a number-crunching whizz-kid computer expert who treats his clients with respect dictated only by their bank accounts. He's a one-off, a generous-hearted, intelligent man who treats every client as an individual and gives each one of them his full attention to detail, no matter what their personal or monetary circumstances. People come to him as if he's the family doctor, ringing our home at all hours and putting tax returns in the porch door after midnight, hoping the night staff may sort them out by 8 a.m. the following morning, by which time the client is already on the phone. Matt takes it all in his stride: he is very laid back, bordering on horizontal, and he always copes with situations in a very practical and personable manner.

At least, he did until January 2001.

We were living in Finchley, North London, in a very

modern apartment, with parquet floors, a roof terrace and jacuzzi bathrooms. It was my dream home, but it was only rented. Most of the time I felt like Cinderella as I knew we couldn't afford to live there permanently, though just to buy a house for the sake of having a mortgage and calling it home wasn't our style. During the 80s, I'd had the misfortune of signing a children's series I had written with a literary agent, who quite frankly had seen this naïve novice coming a mile away and had taken me to the cleaners. To cut a long story short, his own marital problems caused him to take an overdose and die of a massive heart attack, leaving all his worldly goods – and mine! – to his almost divorced wife. So, we'd said goodbye to our house and had begun renting. After a while we started to enjoy it and became quite nomadic. I'm quite quirky and I believe in being positive and optimistic as much as life allows you to be. I lift Matt from his negative trains of thought and he often keeps me grounded. It's a good combination.

Our flat was one of seven in a beautifully built three-storey building. Although I loved living there, my health at that time was on a downward slope. I had suffered at the hands of a so-called spinal surgeon, who had given me two major operations in November and December 2000, letting me believe that if I didn't undergo immediate surgery I would have only a year to live! Mentally I lost the plot, as physically I looked ready for the scrap heap, with drastic weight loss and bandages covering my neck. I was going through the motions of trying to recuperate with all the deadly pain killers. Sleeping was practically a no-go as I couldn't lie down, so I sat up on our comfortable settee against big soft cushions and watched a great deal of television and DVDs. I think I had just fallen asleep, after watching *Frasier* episodes for most of the night to lift my spirits, when our intercom bell rang.

At first I thought it was Andy, our off-the-wall neighbour who lived directly above us. As a radio DJ he was always partying into the small hours of the morning, and on occasions had forgotten his key. I had found a comfortable position, and thought 'Just for a change, try someone else's flat.' I knew Matt and Samantha, our daughter, were fast asleep. They are both very similar in their sleep pattern: head on pillow, dead to the world until the alarm goes off in the morning. Me: even when I'm well, I have trouble going to sleep. My mind works in overdrive and I haven't a clue how to turn off just because it's sleep time. The bell carried on ringing and ringing, as though it was stuck or someone had their finger on the button. I looked at the clock: it was 5.30 a.m. I managed very slowly to move myself off the settee and, putting on my dressing gown, walked to the video intercom, ready to give Andy a piece of my mind. By now Matt and Sam had joined me. The noise had actually woken them up, so you can imagine how loud it was! Looking at the camera we could see a number of men standing on the steps staring into the monitor. Matt picked up the entry phone and a loud voice shouted: 'National Crime Squad for Mr Davidson.' We froze for a moment, looking at each other in amazement. Then Matt pressed the buzzer letting them into the main apartment foyer. We looked through the spyhole of our front door as each police officer showed their identity card before Matt agreed to let them in. Seven plain-clothes policemen and one woman filed into our flat.

The head of this small army looked like Peter Falk's detective character Columbo, complete with creased raincoat and nondescript features on top of a small, stocky frame. He introduced himself as Detective Chief Inspector Martin Clarke. The first words he uttered were to his colleagues. 'This is some apartment: very tasteful, don't you think?' His sycophantic followers all agreed.

I didn't understand the significance of the comment, but quickly said: 'The flat is just a temporary rented let, until we decide where we are going to live on a permanent basis.'

Clarke addressed Matt as though he was a number one threat to society: 'Mr Davidson, we believe you are the accountant to Mr Matthew Carter?'

Matt answered, 'Yes, I am, but could you tell me what this is all about?'

'All in good time. First of all we need to see all files and documents relating to Mr Carter, so show us where you keep the files and we can take them all in your lounge and go through them systematically together.'

Without fear of having anything to hide, Matt took four of the crime squad to his small study and showed them the filing cabinets, giving them carte blanche to take out all the files with Matthew Carter's name typed on the cover. Clarke made himself comfortable on the settee; he obviously wasn't going to spend his time peering into files, that was far too tedious for a high-ranking police inspector. Two other members of his team looked through the book cases at our collection of classic to modern day fiction. Samantha excused herself and escaped into her shower room to quickly wash and dress, and I was given the privilege of showing the policewoman our bedroom. We had at that time a wonderful little dog called Peanut, a bichon frise, but because I was too ill to look after him he was with our close friend Julia.

The policewoman picked up Peanut's basket and threw his pillow in the air. In a gruff near-baritone voice she said, 'Just checking for drugs.'

I couldn't believe she was saying that! She took our bed apart, moving the mattress and reminding me of a large javelin thrower, whose ungainly presence would fill your television screen and cause you to question their gender and whether they had taken any steroids to win the competition. She looked at me ... no, I'll rephrase that ... she looked *through* me and in a horrible tone asked 'What are these?', pointing to the pills on the dressing table. 'Co-Codomol, Co-Dydramol, Tramadol, and what's in the bottle? La Femme

4

Perfume.' She took the perfume and the pills and put them in a plastic bag.

I went into the lounge where Clarke's men had gathered and were all now sitting on the floor with files and papers spread out in front of them. Clarke was still sitting on the settee, lording it over them.

I was feeling bloody angry.

'Mr Clarke, Inspector, Detective, whatever you wish to be called, can you see my neck is bandaged all the way round?'

'Yes, I did notice. Are you ill?'

I wanted to say 'No! This is a new fashion statement! Vivienne Westwood's and Donatella Versace's new winter designer neck coverings!' But I knew it wouldn't help the situation, whatever the situation was! We were still in the dark. So, instead of being sarcastic and volatile, I thought of my mother, who'd taught me that when you're in a crisis the quieter you are, the better the result.

I answered, 'I've had spinal surgery as my back is very bad.'

Clarke sympathized as he had suffered with his back for years.

'In which case, can you please tell that poor excuse for a woman to please give me back my pain killers; they are not hard drugs.'

A few of the squad lifted their eyes up from reading and laughed.

'Sounds like Anne.'

DI Clarke followed me into the bedroom where Anne was looking through my wardrobe.

'Mrs Davidson has had surgery to her back and neck. Put back her pills please and come into the lounge and go through the files.'

I couldn't imagine what she was looking for in the wardrobe; nothing in there would have fitted her, she was built like a tank! With a glare Anne handed me back my pills.

I gave myself a mental pat on the back. I washed quickly, cleaned my teeth and brushed my hair to feel a bit more human, and going into the kitchen I decided to do the British thing and make everyone tea and coffee. I asked what they wanted to drink and they all looked amazed that I would be so hospitable. So, with both Matt and Samantha washed and dressed we all sat drinking tea and coffee, eating rounds of toast and chocolate biscuits as if we were old friends. I looked at Matt and could see how shocked he seemed at what was happening. Obviously there was a major issue with one of his clients. Samantha, on the other hand, appeared extremely angry and hostile. At almost twenty, she was very much her father's daughter, and couldn't believe her wonderful dad was in the middle of some kind of raid...

I looked at the officers all reading different papers and accounts schedules, whilst Clarke carried on munching biscuits. Matt, Sam and I sat opposite him and he looked at the three of us and stated, 'You seem to be a very nice family!'

'We are!' we all said together.

'Well, how did such a nice family become involved with the Carters?'

'First of all, Chief Inspector, we are not "involved", as you put it, with the Carters. Secondly, we are completely in the dark, as we don't understand what they have done wrong to shove such a knock-on effect on to us! And thirdly, my husband has been an accountant forever, well about thirty odd years, and in all that time, he has never encountered any problems whatsoever. Now you come here with the dawn chorus and treat us as number one criminals. Quite frankly I think it's despicable!'

'Mrs Davidson, unless you've been living abroad or in total hibernation, I cannot understand how you don't seem to have a clue about Mr Carter and his activities! He's the most notorious organized crime boss and we've been trying to get him for years, but, through his network of various people who have protected him for years for whatever reason, he has been able to achieve the impossible and give us the complete runaround. Now we at last have the breakthrough we need and that's why we're here.'

'So, in other words, you are assuming that innocent members of the public would know this family, when they clearly keep a very low profile. They obviously don't seek publicity like the Kray brothers, whom everyone has heard of. I can assure you, Chief inspector, if you were to ask any of our friends whether they have heard of Matthew Carter they would all say no. You seem to put us all in your category, but I suspect the only people who would know of him are the police, lawyers, crime reporters and perhaps Ronnie and Reggie Kray. The Davidsons have never, ever heard of Matthew Carter being associated in anything other than antiques.'

'You sound very plausible, Mrs Davidson. Tell me how you all met Mr and Mrs Carter.'

Sam looked at the detective. 'I trained at a private dance and drama school and I used to travel on the school minibus with Jazmin Carter, known as Jaz to everyone. She was a friendly, very streetwise girl, about a year younger than me. We became friends as we lived five minutes from each other. We weren't very close, as we were very different in character. I had my own circle of friends outside school and so did she. We were simply school mates who got on quite well with each other. She came across as very self-assured, which I wasn't, but she was also very kind, generous and likeable. We just didn't gel as mates who would tell each other everything. Sometimes we would go home together and study various dances or acting pieces, and then my parents would pick me up from their house or vice versa.'

'Mr Carter came to collect Jazmin?'

'No, not Mr Carter. Only his wife came.'

'How would you describe Mr and Mrs Carter?'

'I only saw Mr Carter a couple of times and he seemed very friendly. He was also very kind, as Jazmin mentioned to her parents that we needed special dance shoes with split soles from a dancewear shop in Covent Garden that were going to cost more than fifty pounds, and I hadn't told my parents yet as we just received the letter from the school, and Mr Carter had a quiet word with his wife and she said she was taking us both out for tea, and we finished up in Covent Garden, where she marched us into the dance shop and sorted out split sole dance shoes in a few minutes. Although I protested very loudly and said my parents would be annoyed as it was their responsibility to buy my school clothes, both Mrs Carter and Jazmin told me to shut up, and that the shoes were a gift and not a big deal. When I told my parents that evening, my mother phoned Mr Carter and he told her not to think twice about it. He liked me and there was no need to make a fuss, or to reciprocate.'

'Didn't you think a gift like that was rather strange?' Clarke asked me.

'I thought it was very generous, and we were all quite embarrassed by it, but it didn't seem to be out of character for both Mr and Mrs Carter to do something kind on a whim! We had met Mrs Carter a few times, both at school meetings and briefly at our home. She was extremely friendly and very warm and you felt you had known her for years. We had only met her husband once, when we collected Sam and he came to the door, and he appeared to be as friendly as his wife. Matt and I thought he was probably a self-made man who had perhaps landed on his feet by believing in himself. He made sure his family had a good life, and neither he nor his wife saw anything wrong in buying a gift or two for people they liked. He told me to forget about it and said we should just accept the shoes in the spirit they were given.'

I could see Sam was getting upset by Clarke's close scrutiny. I also realized she thought she had innocently introduced us to people who were now inadvertently giving us a whole heap of trouble. Obviously it wasn't anything to do with Sam; we were, perhaps in the light of day, quite naïve as we had absolutely no idea that Matt Carter was allegedly who the Chief Inspector suggested he was! Clarke kept glaring at us, obviously convinced he was making us feel uncomfortable and we would crack under his hypnotic gaze, but he could have stared at us until time ran out, we didn't know anything so what could we tell him? Absolutely nothing!

'Sir, would it be possible for Samantha to show us her room?' asked one of the detectives.

'If that's all right,' said Clarke.

Sam took three of Clarke's men to look at her dance photos and anything that might have a picture of Jaz Carter on.

'Mrs Davidson, please carry on telling me about your friendship with Mrs Carter.'

'As I told you, Adrienne Carter was very friendly. She said she too was studying to be an actress as a mature student; she was at that time in her mid-thirties and I was about eleven or twelve years older. She was taking a foundation course at a college in North London, but because she suffered with word blindness, dyslexia, she asked if I would be able to help her read through her scripts sometimes. I was a writer for children and in my own way quite creative, not a bit numerate like my husband, so I was more than happy to help her. When she was in a play in London our family went to support her and I went on my own a few times, as she was a very gifted actress. In the same way as Sam, we each had our own circle of friends and we never spent any time together socially at weekends. I found Adrienne Carter an interesting woman, complex, vibrant and talented. We got on very well and she was very amusing, with a good sense of humour, which both Matt and I like in people. To be able to laugh at yourself is a great asset, one that I believe the police never have; they take themselves so seriously.'

9

Clarke stared at me in disbelief that I should criticize in any way his beloved police force. 'This is serious work, Mrs Davidson.'

'Oh really! Especially when you raid innocent people because you haven't done your homework properly–'

Matt stepped in just in time. 'Claire, you are digressing. Mrs Carter came to collect Jazmin one evening after school, and told me she was a full-time student, but had been working before in a boutique of some description. As someone at the school had told her I was an accountant, she asked if she would be entitled to a tax rebate. I applied to her college and they sent me the relevant forms, which I filled in and sent to the local tax office. Within a few months she received two and a half thousand pounds. About a year later Adrienne Carter came to see me and said her husband, who is also called Matt, short for Matthew, which mine isn't, needed an accountant, as his had emigrated to I forget where. As I had helped her and our children were friendly it was a positive sign. I remember asking her if her husband was an actor too and she laughed and said, "He dresses over the top like he's on the red carpet, but no, he isn't an actor, he's an antique consultant. When anyone wants to buy an antique, my Matt can advise them on how much to bid, which auction house to go to, and sometimes he is commissioned to buy a painting for a client." It all sounded very impressive and extremely plausible.'

'Chief Inspector, you cannot paint us all with the same brush! Matt knew nothing about Matthew Carter other than what Adrienne had told him, and Sam's and my observations, which quite frankly would have brought anyone to the same conclusion. Whenever Sam was in their house, which on the outside was very ordinary, it was like stepping into an antique shop. Matt would stay in the car and I would go in and wait for Sam if she was finishing a dance routine in Jazmin's bedroom. You couldn't help but notice the glass cabinets of miniature soldiers and Gainsborough paintings that were heavily ornate in their gilt frames. Even Jazmin had an antique bed she was very proud of; it was beautifully carved with figurines all around the headboard and legs. But Sam and I didn't like the house very much; it reminded us of a museum. We are lovers of very modern, airy rooms, but their house was a little on the gloomy side. Still, there was absolutely nothing to suggest to us that Adrienne Carter was telling us a pack of lies, and so Mr Carter became a client.'

Sam came back into the room with the three 'plods'.

'She's been very co-operative, Sir, but there's nothing of any significance in her room.'

'I never thought there would be,' said Clarke. 'It was merely a routine check.'

'I did offer them scissors to cut up my collection of soft animals on the top of my wardrobe, in case there's a haul of diamonds and drugs inside, but for some reason they declined!'

'I can see you have similar sarcasm to your mother,' said Clarke, turning his attention to Matt. 'Tell me, Mr Davidson, how often did you meet Mr Carter to get his accounts?'

'I hardly met him at all! He had a PA who did his bookkeeping for him and he would bring Mr Carter's files over with Mrs Carter and go through the accounts with me. I opened two limited companies for them and quite honestly the work was simple, routine, nothing at all complicated. Once I had completed it and Mr Carter had signed the accounts, the Inland Revenue checked them and there was never, ever anything untoward. It was such an easy, small job to do, I only charged him a small fee of three hundred and fifty pounds. If what you are telling us is true, I would never have worked for him in the first place, but the person you are describing and the one we know could be completely different men! You can only speak as you find, and we always found the Carter family very pleasant, ready to tell a joke, kind to Sam and not in the slightest bit menacing!'

'You were never a threat to him, Mr Davidson. In fact you were very useful, as he used your knowledge, expertise and perhaps as your wife has admitted, your naïvety to his advantage.'

Looking at the time, it was fast approaching 8.30. Three sodding hours we had endured the presence of these ghastly men and Anne; how much longer for God's sake?

'Chief Inspector, if you were in my husband's shoes what would you do now regarding Matthew Carter?'

'I would stop working for him immediately; you don't need him as a client.'

'Fine, that won't be a problem. Adrienne Carter sent us a Christmas card saying they would be spending the New Year in Australia and would stay for the month of January, and possibly some of February. I think the time out there wherever they are is about eleven hours ahead, so while you are here I will try her on the mobile.'

Clarke and his cronies all watched as I picked up an address book and flicked through the pages. Using the cordless landline phone, I tapped in Adrienne's number. By now all the policemen and the woman had closed the files as they had finished going through the papers, and the entire room was silent as everyone waited to see if I would get an answer.

It was like a scene from a movie. 'Please pick up the phone.' I silently willed Adrienne to answer and on the sixth ring, bingo!

'Hello, Adrienne, this is Claire. I'm not ringing to wish you Happy New Year, just to tell you that we've had a complete shock. At 5.30 this morning, we had a visit from eight of the national crime squad demanding to see your files. They're still here three hours later. Therefore Matt cannot work for you anymore. Please tell your husband we've never encountered anything like this in our lives and never want to again!'

I walked with the cordless phone and stood by the side of Detective Inspector, Chief Superintendent, plodding, sodding Clarke, so he could hear Adrienne Carter's reaction. Seeing how horribly cynical he appeared, he probably wouldn't think I was really speaking to anyone otherwise.

The entire room heard, 'Fucking hell! Matt, the fucking crime squad have only gone and paid Claire and Matt Davidson a visit. Claire's on the line now. Matt Davidson can't do your books anymore.' Adrienne's focus switched back to me, 'Please believe us, Claire, we knew nothing about this. I feel sick, I can't hack it. My Matt has been legit for years, but the bastards are still so intent on getting him, they'll do whatever it takes to put the boot in, and bring in good, decent people like you lot. We're so sorry.'

'Well, we won't discuss this anymore on the phone; the call is costing us a fortune. I take it you won't be home yet?'

'No, we're away another few weeks, but please send our sincere apologies to Matt and Sam. We do understand, so very sorry, take care.'

'Satisfied, Chief Inspector Clarke?' I asked, looking at the detective's rather bland expression.

'Yes, that was exactly the right thing to do, although we're not quite finished with you yet, Mr Davidson. We gather you work as a subcontractor in a local office in Finchley, and you do this as well as your portfolio of private clients. I would like to send two of my men with you to pick up any computer discs or extra paperwork you may have on Matthew Carter.'

'Christ, when is this nightmare going to end for Matt?'

Samantha left to go to a dance workshop for the rest of the day, although she looked so tired and worried I couldn't imagine how she would be able to give the class her full attention. I gave her an encouraging hug and whispered, 'Everything will be fine; we'll talk later.'

'Have a rest, Mum. I'll be home early, probably around three-ish. I'm not up to dancing all day!'

Matt was about to leave with two of the police, telling me he was fine, but I could see he looked extremely pale and still shocked, especially now that the bloody plods were going to make an entrance at the office. It seemed so unfair.

'Please make sure you've taken your blood pressure pill.'

'I've taken it, and I'm also coming home early, probably a similar time to Sam. Try and rest, I worry that you won't be all right!'

'Of course I will. I'm going to have a shower and try to think rationally before the district nurse comes to change the bandage. I think it's Isobel today, she's less chatty than Jenny, and today the last thing I need is chat! Would you mind if I tell your mother I had a restless night and she doesn't have to come with food? We have plenty in the freezer, and I really wouldn't be good company.'

'No, I agree. Phone her soon and tell her. See you later.'

The police carried the various files out to their cars, and Chief inspector Clarke promised Matt and me he would contact us with his findings within the next couple of months, once all the files had been checked and double-checked.

The flat was very quiet after they had all left. I showered very carefully, but the simplest task becomes difficult after an operation, and I had to keep my neck dry, which was easier said than done! Slowly changing into a loose, comfortable kaftan, I began to feel almost human.

'Thank you, Sam; you're a darling, loading the dishwasher for me.' I'm muttering away to myself; if anyone heard me they would think I needed to be sectioned. 'Oh and she's left me a note, how thoughtful!'

Hi Mum, I've put boiled water in the china teapot and there's peppermint tea and honey put in your mug all ready for you to enjoy. I've also cut a large slice of Nana's fruit cake (you need fattening up) and all the plates and mugs are in the dishwasher. Plus I've filled the dispenser, so all you've got to do is switch the machine on and then turn yourself off.

p.s. Relax please, you look tired. See you later, Love Sam xxxxxxx

I took the tea and cake into the lounge. After plumping up the cushions, you would never have suspected that the Davidson family had suffered from a dawn raid! The phone rang and it was Matt, just checking I was all right.

'I'm fine, darling. More importantly, how are you bearing up, and have the creeps left the office yet?'

'Yes. They didn't stay very long, thank goodness, maybe only ten minutes. Quite honestly, Claire, there was nothing of importance here for them to take! Anyway, I have two clients to see and then I'm coming home. Have a rest.'

'I am resting. Sam tidied everything away, so there's nothing for me to do. See you later and don't worry.'

Putting the phone down, I closed my eyes and thought about the morning's events. What stupid words I said to Matt. Don't worry! Of course we were all going to worry; how could we not? We'd never been in such a hellish position before. I still didn't understand what on earth was going on. Where was the proof that Matt Carter was a danger to society, as Clarke said he was? It wasn't possible.

I didn't have time to think about the situation as the district nurse arrived. Taking the bandages off without hurting me was an operation in itself!

'Sorry, love! So sorry! You are good! There we are! It's healing very nicely, so I'll put a lighter bandage on your neck for a few days, and gradually we'll be able to put plasters on instead. In a few weeks you'll be as good as new!'

Matt and Sam came home an hour later bringing flowers,

chocolates and authentic Italian lasagne from the local Italian deli.

'Claire! Sam and I have discussed the situation and we both agree the Carter subject has to be put on hold. We are only going to go round in circles until we hear from Clarke and also Adrienne Carter when, or if, she returns. We just want you to concentrate on getting better, so no more is going to be said about what happened today. It will serve no purpose. As I told you on the phone, the police were very quick at the office. Raj was in, but old Taylor wasn't, thank goodness, or I would have had to answer a hundred and one questions from him! It was quiet there today. Our lovely Gladys was engrossed in her new double Dutch filing system, poor old dear. She only comes in two mornings a week and Philip Taylor is such a pain, he changes all her files and she can never find anything, because he confuses her completely. Taylor's secretary June was typing schedules with her radio on, and Pat came in a little after me and went straight into the photocopy room, so I was pleased about that. Sean is away on study leave so Raj and I had a chat when the police had left. I explained to him what happened; he's a very sweet boy, I really like him and trust him. He told me he's only been married for a year, and he and his wife Nina need to make some extra cash, and he wouldn't mind taking over the Carters' papers. I explained to him that, although Mr and Mrs Carter appear fine to us, they could spell trouble, as the crime squad seem hell-bent on getting Matt Carter. But Raj said it didn't matter; he would take a chance. We'll have to wait and see. So, now we're going to enjoy the evening and get a good night's sleep, agreed?'

'I agree. How can I not, with two bosses?'

Eight weeks later, I was actually making a steady improvement. Regular physiotherapy seemed to be the answer, and taking a long weekend break near York, staying in a beautiful hotel with log fires, homemade, wholesome food and decadent, fabulously fattening cream teas. My weight started to creep up, and daily walks with Matt around a pretty lake brought the colour back to my face. However, the icing on the cake was the phone call on Matt's mobile, halfway around the lake. The number display said 'private call'.

'If you don't answer it, you'll never know who it is!'

As Matt made a face, saying he didn't want anyone from the office driving him mad, I took the phone from him – female logic or female curiosity, call it whatever you like. It proved to be the call Matt was waiting for from Chief Inspector Clarke. After a small talk, I handed the phone to Matt. He seemed happy with the conversation, joking about his football team and thanking the policeman. Then he passed the phone back to me as Clarke wanted to reiterate the same message.

'As I have told your husband, Mrs Davidson, all the papers we took away are in order. I am satisfied your husband no longer acts as Mr Carter's accountant, and I am very happy to tell you both to get on with your lives. I wish you well and good luck for the future.'

'Thank you for the phone call, Chief Inspector, we appreciate it.'

That should have been the end of matters, and this story would have been a flimsy eighteen-page folder you would have read in five minutes – not exactly gripping stuff! But life has many twists and turns and you just never know what's around the corner …

I could write many pages telling you how our lives progressed in 2001 and 2002, but why would you want to know? We're not celebrities! No one has heard of us! So I'll skip two years, and hope whoever reads this will pick up the thread as we go along.

2

On 16th January 2003 my mother-in-law Helen celebrated a belated eightieth birthday. Her actual birthday is on Christmas Eve, but getting everyone together at that time proved too difficult. We organized a weekend party at a hotel in Bournemouth, Dorset. The owners, Kate and Keith, are close friends of ours, and Kate had planned the party to perfection. It all went off brilliantly, like clockwork, and that included the wonderful weather. People were walking on the beach in the winter sunshine. That's England for you! Everyone told Helen how well she looked after being ill a few months before, and she said she felt happy that we had put our furniture in storage and come to stay with her, on a temporary basis, until her health improved and we found a permanent home of our own. We were told throughout Helen's weekend how lucky we all were! I had been given a new lease of life and apparently looked very well; Matt was back as Mr Cool, calm and collected; and Sam, looking radiant, was a picture of good looks and happiness. A superstitious person might have said, 'Look out for the evil eye; you never know when it's watching you!' Things can always go pear-shaped!

The 29th April I remember very vividly, as if it was yesterday. The weather had been quite warm for the time of year, and I'd spent as much time as I could writing in Helen's garden. It was a quiet haven and I could concentrate on a pre-school children's series I was trying to devise. I wrote fluidly for about five hours, and then went to pack our

18

overnight cases. Matt and Sam had taken a couple of days off work and were going to stay with Kate and Keith at their hotel in Bournemouth. They were going to a variety show that evening. I, on the other hand, was going on the 9 a.m. coach to Manchester, as I had a two-day hearing at the General Medical Council against the spinal surgeon. I had spent three days in the hot seat in October 2002, and had won the first round battle with 'professional misconduct' written next to the surgeon's name. I realized at the time how fortunate I was when I met a GP who had also believed the very same surgeon, and had been sadly confined to a wheelchair.

Helen was going to enjoy three days of peace and quiet. Although she coped very well on her own, she suffered with asthma and breathing difficulties that could be frightening. Still, she was an independent, spirited soul. With our bags packed, ready to go our separate ways the following morning, I actually went to bed for the first time before mid-night. I'm not sure when I fell asleep, but I do know when the horrific noise woke me up! Does this sound familiar?

The time was 5.30 a.m. The banging on the front door was horrendous. We all opened our bedroom doors at the same time. Helen's dog Toffee, who was sweet-natured and from a rescue home, seemed timid and scared as she stood behind Helen shaking. Sadly, Peanut, our feisty little bichon frise had died, or he would have bounded down the stairs barking at all and sundry. In my sleepy haze, I stupidly had the notion that it could be burglars, until Sam pointed out that it was light outside and that any burglar would be unlikely to wait until early morning and then wake up the entire street. Samantha and I were very afraid, as someone shouted, 'Open the door or we'll bash it in!'

My mother-in-law is a brave lady and she took command, leading the way with Matt close behind her. Sam and I were not so brave, standing halfway down the stairs with Toffee.

Helen unlocked the porch doors and through the frosted glass front door saw the outlines of men. She opened the door with the chain on and was greeted with words we hadn't heard for over two years.

'National Crime Squad – open the door properly.'

Helen undid the chain and one of the men said, 'Another minute, lady, and we would have broken both doors down. We've been banging on your door for over five minutes.'

A tall man stepped forward and asked Matt, 'Are you Mr Matt Davidson?'

Matt stared at him and answered quietly, 'Yes.'

'We are arresting you Mr Davidson for money laundering and false accounting.'

There are no words to describe how we felt! Perhaps anguish comes to mind, but even that isn't a strong enough word! Matt stared at the police in disbelief. My mother-in-law stood rooted to the ground, not able to take in the policeman's words.

Samantha began screaming uncontrollably, 'Arrest murderers, rapists, drug dealers! Why would you pick on a wonderful, completely innocent man? My dad has never done anything wrong in his life! What the hell are you doing? You're all wicked!'

Screaming, crying, shouting, utterly distraught; I shall never, ever forget the look on our daughter's face, a mixture of hatred and despair. The officer was now telling Matt to go and get ready as they were taking him to a police station. Matt was allowed to quickly wash his face and brush his teeth, whilst three policemen held the bathroom door open, watching him. How bloody undignified! What did they think he was going to do, overdose on Listerine mouthwash and advanced whitening toothpaste? A very potent combination I have been told. He had only a few minutes to get washed and dressed, this time with our bedroom door kept open, as their beady eyes watched Matt put on casual clothes as quickly as possible. I was allowed to give him his blood pressure pill – it must have been sky high by now – and after hugging all three of us he was escorted to a black saloon by the same three policemen. We were left with five officers, two of whom were women.

In my blurred, dazed state, I somehow managed to remain quiet, not, I can assure you, my usual stance. But Sam made up for both Helen's and my outwardly calm demeanour. I repeated the same actions as in January 2001: toast, coffee, tea, all put on Helen's dining room table. All the police were accommodated with any files they needed, as Matt had a small portfolio of about thirty clients, and I told them to help themselves and take whatever papers they felt could be of value to them.

Sam had retreated to her room, sobbing quietly, and any soothing noises I tried to make were met with 'Please leave me alone, Mum!' I realized all the talking in the world wouldn't help her until this horrendous situation had been solved.

I sat with Helen and her dog Toffee, who seemed to sense that something was very wrong as she lay in front of Helen's feet looking forlorn. Helen's face had a grey pallor that really worried me; she wasn't showing her feelings but keeping everything contained. It seemed quite unhealthy.

For the life of me, I couldn't understand what was happening. I just couldn't make head nor tail of the situation. How many accountants go through this kind of saga every two years? And, more importantly, who was the client this time who couldn't be trusted? Matt had been so careful with his small list of clientele. I ran through them in my head. A wonderful spinal surgeon, Colin, who had given me complete confidence that I would be well again, and had really put me back together both mentally and physically, had since become a friend and a client, as had his right-hand assistant Adele, who was in charge of a bank of doctors. She was a sparkling, effervescent mixture of friendliness, professionalism and straight talking, a no-nonsense Northern lass, whom we all liked very much. Ron, a printing client, Matt had known for years; he was a salt of the earth kind of man. All three of these people we trusted implicitly, and so I carried on eliminating them all, one by one.

I asked if I could have a quick shower and get dressed (how ridiculous to have to ask permission). I felt very vulnerable with my dressing gown on, especially when the blonde policewoman, the complete opposite of Anne from the 2001 raid, sat drinking her coffee, hair sprayed and moussed, nails varnished and made up ready for a magazine shoot, though, I hasten to add, without the overall glamour.

I washed and dressed, checking on Sam, who was frantically sending text messages to someone and didn't even look up. I went to see if Helen was all right under the circumstances, but although she had finished her tea she was just sitting in the same armchair, staring into space.

'I have asked this question before and you all ignored me. I am asking it again. Can anyone tell us what this is all about?'

Not a word from a soul – was I speaking in Swahili? They were very different from the 2001 bunch, very quiet, plodding through papers and files. One of the men looked up from a file belonging to a lovely dancer friend of Sam, who was then choreographing a West End musical.

'Can't find anything at all in any of these files.'

'Really!' exclaimed Helen before I had a chance to retaliate. 'Do you think we are hiding jewellery, money or whatever it is you are looking for? You can pull up the carpets and the floor boards and I'll give you a spade to dig up the garden.'

'That won't be necessary,' said another officer.

The blonde had finished reading through a bunch of files and said, 'We heard you were helpful and you are. It's very unusual.'

'You appear to be putting us in guilty people's shoes, as my husband is innocent of whatever it is you are looking for!

I have no reason not to give you as much help as possible so this ordeal can be over, but are you able to tell us where my husband is?'

'No, I'm afraid not.' She glanced out of the front window and looked at our fairly ordinary saloon car. 'Check out the bronze Chrysler with the leather seats. That must have cost quite a lot!'

'No, it's a leased car, one of three that the office uses on a three-year basis. I could understand your comment if we had a Rolls Royce or an Aston Martin in the drive, but a Chrysler is a non-pretentious, comfortable car, nothing over the top. It seems to me you are desperately clutching at straws.'

It was now seven o'clock and I was feeling completely useless. We needed advice from a solicitor, and I realized a close friend of ours, Paul Grant, was just that person. He and Matt knew each other from grammar school and he lived five minutes away. As a disciplined personality, he ran every morning like clockwork along Hampstead Heath, so I knew that if I rang him he wouldn't be asleep. As luck had it he was back from his run and getting ready for work. I told him we desperately needed his help and expertise, as we'd had a National Crime Squad raid and Matt had been taken away. Paul simply said, 'Give me five minutes.'

True to his word, he arrived almost immediately. He is a tall man, over 6 ft, and his purposeful strides made the police sit up and take notice. Taking complete charge, he asked for their warrant, demanding to know which police station Matt had been taken to and the name of the client involved.

Helen and I stared in amazement when a quietly spoken policeman said, 'Mr Davidson has gone to Colindale police station and then on to Bristol. This is in connection with Matthew Carter.'

I felt sick to the stomach: of all people, Matthew Carter again! My Matt hadn't worked for the Carters since January 2001.

'I don't understand,' I chimed in. 'Chief Inspector Clarke rang us in March 2001 and told us to get on with our lives as all the papers were in order. He was happy that my husband was no longer looking after Mr Carter's tax and accountancy matters.'

'I'm sorry, Mrs Davidson, I'm not able to say anything on the subject. We are only following orders.'

'Okay, so, what have you found to take away of criminal substance relating to Mr Carter, or even vaguely related to him?'

The police officer said, 'We have found nothing to take.' But one young hopeful, obviously seeking promotion, held a pink form in his hand. He had found it in Adele's file and it related to an investment property to do with Adele's senior citizen parents. They had sold their home in the north of England and retired to Spain.

Oh yes, I thought, what a vital piece of evidence; it would be laughed out of court. What had Adele's inoffensive, sweet parents, who had decided to leave these grotty, cold shores for hopefully a better lifestyle in Spain, to do with Matthew Carter? Was I to understand that anyone who retires to Spain has something to hide? Then I realized that Mr Carter had a brother living in Spain. Perhaps the idiotic police boy thought there was some connection. Well, let him take the form; it wouldn't get him far.

The police all stood up ready to leave.

'You obviously didn't find anything of value,' said Helen.

'No, and we are only taking this to check with our records. You seem to be a very nice family.'

'Yes, we've heard it all before!'

After they left, Paul explained that Matt would need a solicitor in Bristol and that we shouldn't rely on the local man the police would recommend. I couldn't comprehend it all: poor Matt, three hours drive to Bristol, what in the hell for? Colindale was only a twenty-minute drive; why would the police need to take him so far away? It didn't make any sense. Nothing made any sense! A few calls later and Paul had found someone willing to travel by train from Paddington to Bristol, who would catch up with Matt mid-afternoon. Apparently, Neil Harvey was very adept at dealing with high profile criminal cases, and, although Paul didn't know him personally, his reputation was fairly good. Quite frankly we didn't have a choice!

'High profile criminal cases' – I couldn't believe what I was hearing! It all seemed so matter-of-fact to Paul but to us listening it was sheer hell! Neil Harvey had already stated he wanted our assurance he would be paid that week, and depending how long he stayed with Matt it would be in the region of a thousand to fifteen hundred pounds. Helen very kindly said she had some savings and it wouldn't be a problem, and we both thanked Paul for helping us. As a friend, he promised to catch up with us later and to come over in the evening after work. He left me wondering how it was possible to feel so helpless, dependent and unable to control our lives within a split second.

Helen dressed slowly, using her asthma pump as she was sounding very breathless. I realized my mother-in-law had put on a very brave face, and felt sad that she too was suffering, even though she didn't outwardly show it. I did my best at disguising my sadness: powder, paint, a few brushes and lipstick and I appeared on the surface Claire Davidson; but inside I was a crumbling mess!

Sam came down to the lounge at 8.30 and announced she was going to see a counsellor recommended to her by the local health club where Sam was a member. She had been on the phone to a friend who had said this woman could help her, and that Sam would find her easy to talk to. Sometimes you can say what you really feel to someone who doesn't know you!

'I won't be home for a while because I'm going to spend the rest of the day with a friend from the Spa. I'll catch up with you later.'

All this was said with a deadpan expression and a monotone voice. I realized Sam was going to pour her heart out and wanted to give her a hug, but I just said, 'Okay, drive carefully.' I felt very inadequate and to be honest didn't know the magic correct words to say.

'I'll see you later, Mum. Let me know if you hear anything.'

I let her go without any protest, as she looked too terrible for words with her ashen face and a haunted look in her beautiful eyes. I muttered, 'I promise I'll phone you.'

I realized I hadn't told Sam that Matt was going to God knows where in Bristol of all places, because I wouldn't know how to answer her many questions. Until I had spoken to this Neil Harvey and, if allowed, perhaps to Matt himself, I didn't want her worrying any more than she already was.

I knew there was no way on earth that I could go to Manchester, so my chances against the surgeon were practically non-existent. But we were in a crisis and Matt came first, so the bloody man would get his comeuppance one way or another. I rang the Medical Council making my apologies, telling them my husband had become ill and I was sadly unable to testify. The receptionist made the usual noises, and said, 'Sorry to hear he's ill, but the hearing has to go ahead without you anyway. You will be notified by letter of the outcome in a few weeks' time.'

I also rang the coach company. I can't think why, because the moron at the other end must have been at a call centre on another planet. I couldn't hear him or her, so I rang off, feeling even more aggravated. Next I telephoned Matt's office, as even though he wasn't due in until the Friday I thought I should make some excuses, just in case. Thank goodness Raj answered the phone. I told him Matt had some minor chest pains and as we weren't at home, but in

Bournemouth, we didn't want to take any chances, so he was going to have bed rest for a few days. I asked Raj to cancel any appointments Matt had in the diary for Friday. Raj sent his best wishes and, feeling a fraud, though not in the criminal sense, I promised to keep the office informed.

3

The house was now silent, in fact eerily still. Helen and I sat in her lounge staring into space. I kept looking at her mirrored ornate clock hoping for a miracle, that any moment Matt would ring and say, 'Guess what? Typical police incompetence mixed me up with someone else and I'm on my way home!' But it was only 9.30 a.m. and even though it appeared to be much later in the day my gut feeling told me I wouldn't hear from Matt for hours yet.

'I can't imagine what he's going through.' Helen's words interrupted my thoughts and I agreed with her.

'Bloody hell! We can't just sit here and do absolutely nothing; we need to make some phone calls. We're in the dark here and we need answers.'

We both jumped as the phone rang. Helen's younger sister Laura must have heard the dull tone of my voice as I handed the receiver directly to Helen without my usual cheery banter. Helen tried to explain briefly that Matt had been taken away by the National Crime Squad in a dawn raid. Listening to Helen, it all sounded gobbledegook. God knows what sense Laura would be making of it. All I heard was Matt's aunt loudly exclaim, 'It's a complete nonsense! You couldn't have anyone more innocent than Matt. What are you talking about, Helen?'

'They're our sentiments exactly,' answered Helen, 'but I had better keep the line free in case we get a call from Matt so I'll speak to you later.'

I realized I needed support from friends and perhaps their

28

thinking on what was happening to Matt. I knew the women in his life were too close to the subject to perhaps think in a rational way. Carol and Mike sounded amazed by my news, and as they are very good friends to both Matt and me on an equal basis, their input was very valuable. Mike promised to come over later that morning. Geoff, on the other hand, had never been married. He was a fun-loving character on the surface, who enjoyed being the centre of attention at parties and keeping everyone amused, but I always suspected there was something far darker and deeper lurking under his many extrovert layers. He said he was astounded and would also come over to see us.

I cannot ever remember sitting still for so long and Helen and I were relieved when Mike arrived just before midday. As usual he was his upbeat, cheerful self. Mike's personality is very outgoing, kind, warm and friendly. He's extremely like-able and my mother-in-law was very happy to see him. She quickly made herself busy in the kitchen, making tea and cut-ting her homemade cake. She enjoys cooking and is very good at it. I explained to Mike the morning's activities and at first he looked horrified, but after a while his expression softened.

'You know, thinking about it all logically, Claire, it could all be blown up completely out of proportion. I remember a long time ago a pal of mine was carted off to the local cop shop. He was detained for a while but then they had to let him go. They had no choice, they didn't have anything on him to book him. So you wait, Matt will ring this afternoon and he'll be back here later today.'

'I hope you're right, Mike. However, through past experience with Matthew Carter, I don't feel it's quite so simple.'

'Be positive, isn't that your motto? And phone us when you hear what's happening. Carol's had to go out this morning to a meeting, but we're both home after five today.'

I thanked him for the pep chat and he rushed off. Within

five minutes of his departure, Geoff arrived on his motor bike. He lives in south London, and the traffic from Vauxhall through to the Finchley Road had been its usual heavy self, 'Otherwise, Claire, I would have been here an hour ago.'

I thought it was a good thing that he'd been held up. Mike is very friendly, but I wasn't too sure if Geoff was flavour of the month with him. It was possible that Mike saw him in a different light than we did, and in fact he was right, as will be shown later on. But, at that time, Geoff was a friend, and his presence was appreciated by Helen and me.

Helen went through a similar ritual as before, adding sandwiches this time as it was after 1 p.m. I went through the sorry saga with Geoff and he appeared visibly shaken. He had always got on very well with Matt, and vice versa, and for the past few years he'd brought any tax papers over to Matt, who helped him immediately, whilst discussing their favourite football teams.

'Claire! I can't get my head around this! He'll ring soon, once the solicitor gets there, and we'll all go and meet him at Paddington station. It sounds to me a complete cock-up with the police.'

'Yes, from your mouth to God's ears, let's hope this Neil Harvey knows what he's doing!'

'Another thought, why Bristol?'

'I wish I knew, but I have absolutely no idea at all. It's a bloody mystery. There's enough police stations in London; it sounds as though the police are playing their mind games with decent people.'

'It's bloody outrageous!' It was a favourite word of Geoff's, and in this instance a very apt one.

'It's no good just guessing, we don't know the answers. I'll put the television on, and let's watch some rubbish until we hear from Matt.'

I was half watching a Gene Kelly escapism musical, where everything is fine and dandy, when the phone rang. Matt's voice had an edge and an urgency to it. 'Claire! What do I do about a solicitor? The police have said they will help me and get a local man, but I was allowed one call and I thought perhaps you had sorted someone out for me.'

'Matt, I have. At least Paul has. His name is Neil Harvey and he should be with you very soon. He's travelling by train from Paddington. Paul said not to have the police recommend a solicitor.' I then rambled on and said stupid things like, 'Are you all right? Where are you exactly?'

'I can't talk now, Claire. Thanks for dealing with everything.'

'We all love you, Matt, and both Mike and Geoff send their best. Please ask Mr Harvey to phone me when he arrives.'

I turned to Helen. 'Oh, Matt's voice sounded shaky. Christ, how long does it take to get to Bristol by train? Matt seemed desperate. I'm worried! Sorry, Helen, I don't mean to make you feel more alarmed than you are, but this is all so peculiar. I can't believe someone as innocent as Matt is being put through some horrible ordeal! I hope the bloody man turns up soon, or else some local yokel will have to do, and that doesn't sound good enough. Matt's voice was muffled, and he chose his words very carefully, so he obviously couldn't say what he wanted to. The bastards must be in the room with him. This isn't helping you, Helen, is it? Sorry, I don't mean to make you feel worse, but I have to tell you the truth and Matt sounds, how can I put it, not exactly scared, but completely out of it!'

Helen nodded. 'The whole thing is disgraceful. Perhaps a London solicitor will be an asset for Matt and get to the bottom of it all quickly.'

Geoff paced up and down the lounge. Toffee, who was very happy to see visitors, paced with him, and Helen and I sat waiting for the blasted phone to ring.

At just gone 3 p.m. Neil Harvey telephoned. I had never heard of him before, but there was something about his manner that I disliked as soon as he began speaking. Very matter-of-fact, he explained that he had only just arrived, as the police station was in the middle of the countryside or, as he put it, 'in the centre of nowhere' and not in the centre of Bristol as he had thought. He emphasized that it had been a taxi ride away, and I promptly told him to please add it to his bill. I also told him that the police had taken only one sheet of paper from our house, and that it didn't have anything to do with Matthew Carter, but belonged to a client's mother. I asked him to look into it. He said he would keep it in mind as a piece of useful information when the time was right, and that he would be sitting with Matt and the police very soon, but had a sneaky feeling that Matt would be charged. He agreed to phone us again as soon as the session with the police was over.

'Claire, what's wrong? You've gone very pale.'

'I would like to scream! This Harvey's a bugger, I'm sure of it. He has automatically assumed without hearing any valid facts that Matt will be charged! He said Matt is at a police station out in the wilds. What is my husband doing out in the sticks? What is he, a mass murderer? It seemed to surprise Harvey as much as me. He appears to me to be very money orientated, as he let me know almost immediately that he had to take a taxi from the centre of Bristol. You must have gathered that by my answer. It's all so detached. I'll have to ask more questions when he calls again, after he's had time to talk to Matt and the crappy crime squad. I feel as though our lives have been put on hold, as if we have been taken over and everything else is secondary.'

Helen looked at my face and perceptively noticed my expression. 'I'll make some tea, with sugar. It's good for shock, and you look like you've had one!'

'Thanks, Helen. Perhaps I'm overreacting to Neil Harvey's attitude. He doesn't sound a compassionate person at all. Still, I suppose to be fair he's a solicitor; this is just another job to him, and he's been thrown into the deep end, and doesn't have a clue about Matt, whether he's honest or not. Perhaps I am judging him harshly, but I can't take to him on the phone, so God knows how I will react if I have to see him in person!'

'I'm really worried about Matt,' I whispered to Geoff as Helen left the room. 'I know I'm reading between the lines and making two and two six. But I think the police have conveniently lumped our Matt in with Matthew Carter. Whatever happened to the wonderful British judicial system where you are supposed to be innocent until proven guilty? This seems to be the other way round, it's sick making!'

'It doesn't sound very encouraging, I admit,' agreed Geoff, 'but we have to wait and see. It's no good coming up with answers when we don't know the questions.'

'Very profound. I just feel helpless. I don't know how to help Matt, and leaving it to Neil Harvey to use his legal brain isn't much to feel positive about. Still, he's all we have, so let's hope he can get somewhere for Matt's sake, as thinking too much about what he could be going through is taking away my energy.'

Countdown came on and Geoff and Helen pushed their minds into working out maths and words. I never watch the programme, I find it very boring, so I opted for being bored while concentrating on a silent phone. Right at the end when the conundrum word flashed on the screen my brain clicked into gear and I got the answer without even thinking about it.

'See? It's good for you, Claire. You have to try and take your mind off the situation.'

Just before 6 p.m. Neil Harvey's voice boomed down the phone.

'As I suggested earlier, Mrs Davidson, your husband has been charged, and so I shall have to find myself a hotel so I can be here tomorrow. The police will have another day of questions and your husband will need me. I will give you a

33

call in the afternoon and let you know when a hearing will take place in court.'

My voice didn't sound like me as my throat had suddenly gone dry. 'Mr Harvey, what are the charges against my Husband?'

'Off the top of my head I can't remember all four, but I know two of them are false accounting and money laundering.'

'It's total rubbish! My husband is completely innocent; these charges have been fabricated!'

'That may be so, Mrs Davidson, but unfortunately the police don't see it that way. We shall have to see what happens tomorrow. I have to go as I must check into a hotel.'

'Thank you, Mr Harvey. Please send Matt our love.'

What did I thank him for? He was off to check into a five-star deluxe hotel while Matt was banged up in some revolting hellhole police station! Helen and Geoff didn't need me to explain the conversation; they had understood it practically word for word.

Sam came home and I tried to soften the blow. I think I said, 'Although Dad's been charged today, the solicitor will see what can be done tomorrow.'

'Where is Dad now?'

'At the police station, that's all I know.'

'Oh, I hope he's all right. I'm so worried about him,' and Sam, refusing any comfort from us or any food, went to her room.

'She'll make herself ill and that won't help her or anyone else,' said Helen.

'We have to leave her to her own devices. She is old enough, as she keeps on telling us, and I'm sure if she was hungry she would eat, I hope! Actually, I don't want to eat either. I can't get the image of Matt out of my mind, and I haven't phoned Kate and Keith. They must be wondering where Sam and Matt are.'

I told Kate a white lie, that Matt had a few chest pains and we didn't think it a good idea for him to travel to Bournemouth. Kate is such a warm, giving person and she sent Matt loads of love. I promised to phone her in a day or two. If only she'd known the truth, I feel sure she would have had a number of choice words to say about the arrest, the police and the whole lousy situation!

I knew I couldn't speak to Matt – he'd had his only call to me earlier – so I wasn't able to grasp how he was dealing with the horror story and whether he was being looked after. Was he eating? Were they being horrible to him? What was I thinking? My mind was in overdrive and I didn't know how he was going to get through the ordeal, because it had to be an ordeal: one minute you are living what you consider to be a pretty average normal life and the next … you're carted off at dawn like Jack the Ripper. You are considered a criminal in the warped minds of the police, so to add insult to injury you're made to look like a criminal. Best not to shave or wash properly then! But if you are lucky you are given a few seconds to have a spit wash and brush your teeth, then you go on a mystery ride to some ghastly remote police station hours away, and one phone call is all you are allowed before you are charged with God knows what!

Taking me away from my thoughts, Geoff said he needed to get home. I promised I would contact him the next day and give him an update. Sam, Helen and I managed to eat soup, and Sam said she was tired and would try and rest in bed. She had taken a week's holiday from work, as she needed some quiet time and because she wanted 'to be around for Dad'. Some holiday! I thought. Well, hopefully we'll have a holiday when all this fiasco is sorted. I promised to wake her immediately if I heard anything positive that evening, even though we all knew it wasn't going to happen.

At 9 p.m. Paul came over to find out what was happening to Matt. Helen, looking drained, said she would relax in a bath and then go to bed, as the day's early morning wake-up call was taking its toll. I explained as best as I could my telephone conversations with Matt and Neil Harvey, and when I told Paul that Matt had been charged he phoned Neil Harvey's mobile and was on the phone for ages. I sat opposite him, trying to gauge the conversation, but I could only hear snippets. Nevertheless, Paul's expression was a dead giveaway: I was able to understand that Harvey was voicing his opinion about my husband and not in a positive way. I could hear his pompous tones through the phone as the house was very quiet. 'Mr Davidson should have known in the first instance whom Adrienne Carter was married to.' He then appeared to be trying to justify the despicable charges! My anger must have shown on my face as Paul looked rather uncomfortable. His voice was the opposite to Neil Harvey's, quiet and non-threatening, and I noticed his only answers to Harvey were yes and no. It sounded to me as though Harvey hadn't listened to Matt and even worse didn't believe him. Some bloody awful solicitor he seemed, and a crappy judge of character. I wouldn't want him to represent me if I was ever in trouble, because the way I was feeling I might be up for murder!

Paul finally replaced the receiver. In a fit of temper I told Paul what I thought. 'What in hell's name is he saying or doing for Matt? Bloody nothing! You have known Matt from your school years, a long time. You know what a good and decent man he is! Many of Matt's clients need hand-holding, and figures come very naturally to Matt. The Carters were no different to any other client, it was all part of Matt's working day! Harvey doesn't know Matt at all, and I heard a few of his snide comments. Please don't take this the wrong way, as you have been wonderful, but I don't know him and I don't like him. I understand we needed someone quickly, and I am sorry to sound ungrateful, but he just wants the money and sod Matt!'

'Claire! It doesn't look good at the moment for Matt. The police are hell-bent on making the charges stick. Obviously we will know more tomorrow, but if bail monies are required I can probably put ten thousand pounds in the pot. I'm not supposed to, because solicitors shouldn't get involved that way, but I'll speak to Miri tonight and ask her opinion.'

Miri was away visiting her elderly mother in a nursing home and Paul hadn't been able to tell her about Matt. Miri's reaction I felt sure would be shock horror. She was a very perceptive, strong-minded woman, and she would think the system was in need of a shake-up, putting someone as innocent as Matt in such a frightening situation. I like Miri and Paul very much; they were a perfect balance for each other and I felt sure she would agree to help if she could.

I thanked Paul for everything he was doing for us, and, although he said he had to be in a local court over the next two days, I promised to leave a message on his mobile and bring him up to date as soon as I heard anything from Neil Harvey.

An hour or so later, having spoken to Carol and Mike, who both gave me rational answers to my very irate and probably irrational questions, I decided to hit the brandy bottle, which for me was unheard of, but I needed something to dull the ache. Two small glasses of brandy and a splitting head later, I tried mechanically going to bed. I looked at Matt's football programmes lying in a tidy pile on the shelf. I could hear Sam's television on very quietly, and Helen going back and forth to the bathroom, and I just lay on the bed without getting undressed, going over and over old ground. None of us were going to sleep that night. And never mind that, how was Matt? Was he sleeping and if so where? The bed seemed empty without him and I felt very lonely. With the small bedside light on for company, lonely became sad. I could not begin to find the right words to describe it. I clock-watched through the night. The brandy had only touched the surface of how I felt, and I wasn't able to sleep at all. At 5.30 a.m. I expected the bell to ring and keep on ringing, and when it didn't I was quite surprised. I couldn't lie on the bed any longer and at just after 6 a.m. I had showered, dressed and put on make-up to try and disguise my complete lack of sleep. I met my mother-in-law going down the stairs quietly. She too was fully dressed, and between us we made toast and for Helen a pick-me-up cup of tea and for me caffeine coffee. We now felt able to do battle for round two.

4

Thursday took on a similar pattern to the day before. Helen talked on the phone to her sister, letting out her frustrations. I took various calls from acquaintances who thought Matt wasn't feeling well and was having a few days rest. I acted quite well through the small talk and let them believe what they wanted to. I took in Matt's post, answered a few letters on his behalf and realized that sitting by the telephone just waiting for news was soul-destroying. By late morning Sam came down, saying she was going back to the counsellor and would be out for a few hours, but that if anything happened in the meantime ...

'I know, I'll call you immediately.'

'Before you ask me, Mum, I came down earlier and took cereal and orange juice to my room, so I have eaten breakfast. I've washed, made my bed and now I'm ready to try and talk my heart out and hope a miracle will happen in the meantime.'

I can only say my heart felt very heavy as I waved Sam goodbye. Although I'm not religious, I silently prayed to my mother, father and father-in-law to give us the courage to deal with whatever was in store for us to overcome.

Neil Harvey's call came after lunch. 'Mrs Davidson, there will be a hearing tomorrow morning at 9.30 at Bristol magistrates' court.'

'Can I be there please and can I also bring a change of clothes for my husband?'

'Yes, to both of those questions. I suggest you book a hotel for tonight and try and get to the police station before 10 p.m. It will be too difficult for you to get to the police station in time in the morning. You can bring a suit and a wash bag with his shaving cream, razor, etc. and then tomorrow morning I will meet you in the entrance hall of the court at 9. I am six feet tall, with not a lot of hair, and I'll be wearing a navy blue suit.' He rattled off the police station and court address. I asked him to send Matt our love and that was that.

I left Sam a message on her mobile telling her I was trying to find out train timetables as I needed to go to Bristol very soon. Then I rang Carol and Mike and promised to let them know what was happening in court. They said they would be in all day and that if I needed to raise bail monies they would help. In my still non-religious state, I blessed them. Geoff rang me, as he was getting impatient waiting for my telephone call. I told him I was in a hurry and he offered to come with me to Bristol for moral support. I thanked him for his kindness and, taking a small case down from the top of the wardrobe, I packed it with Matt's best Italian suit, socks, boxers and wash things. I put a packet of wine gums in the case and a letter from all of us on the top, telling Matt how much we loved and supported him and that I would see him tomorrow.

Sam came rushing in. 'Mum! Don't get a train ticket, I will drive you to Bristol and stay with you overnight, but I don't think I can face going into court tomorrow and seeing Dad. I would probably break down and that wouldn't help him at all, so, if you don't mind, I have a friend at university there and he will spend the morning or day with me, until it's time to drive home.'

I hugged Sam until she could hardly breathe. 'Thanks, darling, I really appreciate it, and if you don't mind, Geoff has offered to come as well.'

'That's fine with me. What will Nana do?'

'I'll be fine. All I want is for you to bring my son home. I'll be busy shopping as I'll make dinner and probably visit Laura during the day. Don't worry about me; just get cracking and go.'

I had booked a hotel in the centre of Bristol, which apparently was only a five-minute walk from the court. Geoff arrived with a message from his brother Craig, who sent love and good wishes, emphasizing what a load of rubbish it all was. I told Geoff to thank his brother and felt a little encouraged by the few kind words. Then I thought about Inspector Clarke and his false promises in 2001. He'd told us to go forward with our lives, but now we were completely stuffed!

Sam was ready by 5 p.m. and, after filling up with petrol at a local garage, she drove to Bristol as if on autopilot. I sat in the back of the car and glanced occasionally at her profile as she drove silently along the M4, with music playing very quietly in the background. For Samantha Davidson that was unheard of! Geoff, after trying to make polite conversation, gave up, seeing that neither of us was in a talkative mood. Although the traffic was quite heavy in the rush hour, it moved at a steady pace and we arrived in Bristol at 8.30. We had to park at a public designated car park by the side of the hotel, and walk across the road to the front entrance. After signing us all in, I left almost immediately to find a cab to take me to the dreaded police station. I had brought two hundred pounds in case we needed it, and hailed a taxi, hoping to find a local driver who knew the surrounding area. No luck: the only driver I could find looked surprised when I handed him the address.

'I don't know exactly where it is, but I know it's about twenty to thirty minutes' drive. Let me look it up in my local map and then we'll go. Are you a solicitor going to see your client this time of night?'

What a question! I just answered yes and hoped my

monotone answers would stop him from constantly talking. He didn't seem to be too bothered whether I answered him or not. He carried on quite happily talking about the weather, how he would love one day to travel, and how he hoped his son would one day become a lawyer, 'Just like you, Madam. The police station where we're going now is well-known for the elite in criminal activities. So your client can't be a petty thief; he must be pretty major. I realize you can't answer that.'

I acknowledged his logic with a forced smile that took a great deal of effort, as here was a total stranger thinking Matt was a big time criminal! Ludicrous, absurd, ridiculous!

Finally, after what seemed like an age, we arrived in what I can only describe as a grassland area, with one gloomy, bungalow-style building standing out like a sore thumb with nothing else around it. The driver promised to wait for me as I told him I was only delivering something and wouldn't be very long. The first thing I noticed walking up the path with Matt's case were the tiny windows with bars, and I could imagine Matt behind one of them. I felt sick and wondered what sort of test this was. Walking into the primitive police station, I suddenly felt cold. I rang the bell on the counter and waited for a policeman or woman to come to my aid. I looked at the clock – it was almost 9.40 – and after a few minutes a policeman of middle age actually smiled at me. I explained who I was, that I had driven from London and brought my husband a change of clothes and a wash bag, plus a handwritten note from his family that I hoped he would be allowed to read.

He said, 'Of course, no problem at all. Your husband is a very nice man.'

It was a common observation from people when they met Matt. If even the police thought so, what on earth was creepy Clarke playing at? I politely thanked him and asked him to give Matt my love. He assured me he would, and I thought he appeared very amicable. I must have been losing my mind, how could he have been? What sort of decent human being becomes a hard-nosed police officer with no conscience whatsoever?

Walking slowly out of the grotty station, I felt worse than I did going in. How could I leave my husband in such a terrible Dickensian place, banged up for what? All sorts of horrible thoughts came into my head but I had to try and keep a detached look as the taxi driver kindly jumped out to open the passenger door for me. I thought about Neil Harvey, who was no doubt staying in a five-star hotel, eating smoked salmon, drinking wine and sleeping in a very comfortable bed. Lucky bastard, what was he going to do to help Matt?

The driver's words interrupted my thoughts. 'Did you see your client? Or is he in solitary confinement? This is so interesting for me, I must be the first foreign taxi driver to take a legal person to this station. It's reputation is well known and I can eat out on this for a while.'

Poor man, it wasn't his fault I felt like adding him to my extensive hit list! But, with outward calm and self-control, God knows how, I just said, 'No, I'm afraid your imagination is working in overdrive. My client is definitely not dangerous, and I'm not allowed to talk anymore about legal matters due to data protection, and client confidentiality.'

That piece of uninteresting information shut him up immediately, and he drove the whole way to the hotel in silence. Paying him with a fairly good tip, which he thanked me profusely for, I rushed in to the hotel. Sam and Geoff were waiting in one of the rooms. I explained as best I could that the station was quite far away. I didn't say anything about bars on windows. Sam looked so pale and tearful that I needed to soften the harsh reality. I couldn't have borne it if she'd become ill because of the ordeal. I would have had two people to worry about and Helen as well. I felt very anxious for Helen; she managed to put on such a brave face, but what she must have been going through, her only son, a kind, warm and generous man, being used in such a despicable way? How would any caring mother feel?

None of us felt like eating a meal, but we went for a walk and found a late night corner shop, buying comfort food and drinks. We couldn't be bothered to spend an hour or so walking around aimlessly exploring the sights of Bristol, so we just went back to the hotel. Geoff said he was tired and would see us at 7.30 for breakfast.

Sam and I undressed, even though we knew that any sleep would be fitful. Most of the night was spent airing our feelings, and when my alarm went at 6 a.m. I could only have slept for about an hour. I quickly showered and dressed in my favourite deep purple satin shirt over grey wool trousers. I was determined to wear a bright colour so Matt could see I wasn't sitting in court all doom and gloom. Carefully putting on my make-up with a large magnifying mirror held in front of my face, I tried to disguise the dark rings that had formed under my eyes. As any woman knows, a magnifying mirror has no mercy! Sam was very quiet, I think because we had spoken at length during the night and there was nothing to add. We met Geoff and tried to eat a basic continental breakfast.

'Everything seems to taste of cardboard. Not that I make a habit of eating it too often,' I hasten to add.

'When Matt comes back with us today, you'll enjoy eating again.' I nodded in agreement, hoping Geoff was right.

We checked out, put our bags in Sam's boot and she drove us to the court. She was meeting her friend Tim just around the corner from the court house, and I promised I would call her as soon as I knew what was happening, or else in the lunch break. There was just time for a hug and a brief word or two. 'Be strong, Sam, it's going to be all right and Dad will be in the car with us going home today.'

Geoff and I went through the security rigmarole and

walked around the court foyer, if you can call it that! We looked completely lost and out of place.

It was exactly 9 a.m. and there were small groups of people talking quietly amongst themselves. Some had their official-looking solicitors with them, with their briefcases stuffed to the brim with case notes. There were various notice boards dotted around the walls displaying court times and court numbers, but nothing jumped out with the names Carter or Davidson. I looked around and noticed Mr and Mrs Carter's daughter Jazmin standing by the side of an older woman and man. They were talking quite socially, as if they were about to attend a concert.

'I don't understand how they can be so chatty when I feel like I'm dying inside.'

'Claire, you must understand that this is just another day at the office for these people. They probably live right on the edge and their daughter is used to it, or else she went to acting school with Samantha and is maybe a better actress than she is given credit for. It's probably just streetwise bravado on her part.'

Before I could answer Geoff's wise words, Jazmin turned round and saw me. The surprised look on her face was easy to read, as she'd clearly not expected to see me at the court.

'Claire, what on earth are you doing here? Have you come all this way to support my parents? I thought you were supposed to be up in Manchester for a few days at a health issue case?'

I looked at Jazmin, dressed in a pretty designer outfit. She was very mature for her age, but there was still an air of innocence around her that was endearing and I felt unable to be angry with her. It wasn't her fault; she was also an innocent victim. I answered politely, 'I'm not here to support your parents; I'm supporting my husband.'

She looked visibly shocked. 'What? Your Matt's here as well?'

'Yes, we were woken up on Wednesday at the wonderful time of 5.30 a.m. and within minutes he was taken away.'

'Fucking hell, Claire! My mum and dad will be shocked when they see him in the court.'

'Not as shocked as we are!'

'Oh, this is my aunt and uncle,' and she rattled off names. Through politeness I nodded my head, but I couldn't tell you what their names were as I wasn't concentrating. Jazmin put a hand on my arm. 'It will be all right, Claire. Matt's completely innocent, and so are my mum and dad. I'm sure he'll be free today.'

'I hope so, Jazmin.'

'I'll see you later, I must talk to Jenny Thornton's mother.'

'Bloody hell, Geoff, how many people have they brought to Bristol?'

'We'll find out soon. Do you know who Jenny Thornton is?'

'Yes, I'll tell you about her soon. I think Mr Harvey is coming towards us.'

Neil Harvey didn't disappoint me in his description, it was spot on. He looked like he sounded, brusque, no frills, a complete lack of old-fashioned charm. He did not seem to be a personable man and I knew that I wouldn't be able to speak to him. I introduced myself and Geoff as a family friend, and the solicitor said he would take us to the waiting area as the court should begin on time. Geoff and I would be able to sit at the back of the court as it would be quite busy towards the front, with the defendants' solicitors and some clerks as well.

'Mr Harvey, how many defendants are there?'

'Six, with your husband. This is a big case, Mrs Davidson, and it will probably take up most of the day, so be prepared for a long wait. By the way, I do have an encouraging faxed letter from Paul. He has written about Matt in very glowing terms as a character reference and if I am able I will read it out to the magistrate or give it to him to read.'

'Yes, Paul knows Matt well. That was kind of him and is

46

very much appreciated. I think he would have come with us but he had to be in court himself today.'

Mr Harvey charged ahead and we quietly followed him. The waiting area was a soulless place, with uncomfortable benches, rotten for the back, and a narrow corridor with people walking up and down talking quietly into their mobile phones. Geoff and I sat opposite a bearded man with quite long hair, but although he smiled at us his smile didn't quite reach his eyes. There were two other men with him and they were talking animatedly to Jazmin Carter. They were obviously Mr and Mrs Carter's friends.

'This is horrendous, Geoff. I can't believe this is happening.'

We watched as Jazmin spoke to a suit with a briefcase, obviously a solicitor, and she went with him into the court with the rest of her entourage following behind.

'Come on, Claire, we had better go in as well.'

5

Geoff and I sat at the back as suggested by Mr Harvey. There were about twelve rows of seats, all taken up with God knows who. I certainly didn't have a clue. I tried to take in the surroundings: the magistrate was sitting at the far end of the court, and to the left of him Clarke and his merry band of men sat in their own designated area. By the side of them were the court stenographer and the clerk to the court, and in front of the police was the stand where you swore your oath.

Geoff said, 'Claire, you are looking the wrong way. Look to your right: Matt is sitting in the middle of the dock looking extremely smart and professional whilst the others around him all seem to be in need of a change of clothes and a good wash!'

I forced my head to turn to the right as I was very afraid of seeing Matt's reaction when he saw me. I counted six defendants sitting behind a long glass window with my lovely husband stuck in the middle of them. As Geoff had pointed out, he was the only one dressed immaculately; the others were all in casual tracksuit clothes. I couldn't understand why they hadn't been given permission to change. I tried to catch Matt's attention, but Geoff and I could see that, although he was there physically, his mind was somewhere else. All six had court officers sitting behind them. Two men sitting by Matt I had never seen before, and I knew Matt didn't know them. Matthew Carter's stance was unreadable, but next to him Jenny Thornton looked as though she had been crying and Adrienne Carter was the nearest to me.

Adrienne turned towards me and I could see she looked very pale and perhaps a little uncomfortable as she silently mouthed 'I'm sorry'. I didn't know how to respond as I wasn't ready nor able to reply to that; my husband was plonked in the centre of a National Crime Squad hit! Except in Matt's case, they had missed – big time!

I couldn't speak for Geoff, but I was totally ignorant of the rules and regulations of how a court works. Solicitors were talking amongst themselves, and Mr Harvey came over to me just to give me a brief understanding.

'The Crown Prosecution solicitor will speak first, outlining their case, and then DCI Clarke will answer questions from the defendants' solicitors. Each solicitor will have five to ten minutes' questioning time and then a decision will be made regarding bail.'

I knew there were loads of questions I should have asked him but somehow I couldn't get my head into gear. I kept looking over at Matt but he looked spaced out, in a trance; it's the only way to describe it. I hoped it was his way of coping.

The magistrate began to speak. He had such a horrible tone of voice and such a harsh, surly expression that I half expected him to be wearing the old-fashioned death sentence black cap! Thank goodness it wasn't the 1950s and that he wasn't a High Court judge. Christ, my imagination was running wild.

The solicitor for the prosecution was a small, insignificant man and his voice was equally so. If it had been an audition for the theatre he would have failed immediately. It was obvious to all of us that public speaking wasn't his forte, as no one could hear a word he was mumbling. Halfway through his dire monologue, Neil Harvey in his very distinct voice called out, 'We can't hear you!'

Another solicitor stood up and reiterated it. The CPS solicitor tried to make his voice carry around the court room, but after a few words he drifted off again. I looked at Geoff, who grinned and said a few choice words about unheard of heckling in a civilized court room. Judging by Matt's face, though, it wouldn't have made any difference if the man had been a world-famous orator; Matt was definitely in a world of his own. People were laughing out loud as though we were at a comedy instead of at a court hearing.

'Do you realize, Claire, it's almost 11? How much longer is the little git going to ramble on for?'

The magistrate must have agreed with Geoff as he suddenly called out, 'Can you speak up? It's very hard to hear everything you're saying and you appear to have written out a bible. You need to condense it; time is getting short and I haven't even been given your name.'

Everyone kept very quiet, waiting to hear his name. This time he actually managed to speak in a louder voice. 'I would rather not say, Sir.'

The magistrate looked quite dumbfounded. 'On what grounds?'

'I don't want the defendants to know my name because of who they are.'

'What a wanker!' someone said in front of us.

The magistrate sounded very irritated. 'Well, my name is Robert Evans. Everyone can hear that, including the people in the dock, therefore you will tell the court your name.'

The solicitor, although put on the spot, was much tougher than he sounded, and refused again to say his name. He scribbled something down for the clerk to give to the magistrate. At first, I had thought this was a good start for the defendants, the solicitor for the prosecution being a complete idiot. If the magistrate got fed up with him, it could be a good sign for us! Now I realized this was all part of the CPS plan: their own solicitor pretending to be intimidated by the defendants made it all sound very sinister. My fears were realized when the magistrate read the note and changed direction immediately, not saying another word and giving the creep the upper hand to carry on whispering for what seemed like an age.

At almost midday, Detective Chief Inspector Clarke was called.

'He wouldn't know the truth if it jumped up and hit him squarely on the chin. That's the bastard who lied to us in 2001!'

'Don't be naïve, Claire. That's what the police do, they lie.'

'Isn't there an honourable, responsible, decent policeman out there? Surely when you are so irresponsible you just book anyone to fill your target sheet, regardless of how it affects innocent men or women and their families? It's disgusting!'

'Columbo' Clarke, wearing the same raincoat he had on in 2001, went on the stand. Hand placed over the Bible, he swore he was telling the truth, the whole truth...

I don't know why lie detectors aren't allowed in an English court. They say they are not reliable, concrete or, more importantly, truthful. But Clarke's evidence against Matt would have been blown away in a minute with the use of one! The bloody court system in this country is antiquated: we are way behind other countries, and magistrates and judges automatically believe if your name is Clarke or you are an unnamed CPS solicitor, Mr Incognito, you should be honorable. However, this doesn't appear to be the situation.

Clarke had to read out a statement, which this time we could all hear.

'On 30th April 2003 I sent officers to Mr Matthew Carter and Mrs Adrienne Carter, Ms Jennifer Thornton, Mr Brian Dorfmann, Mr David Edwards and Mr Matthew Davidson.'

'He's got that wrong; my husband is just Matt, not Matthew. And of all the names to choose from! Matthew Carter calls himself Matt, so it's possible Clarke is mixing both of them up somehow.'

Clarke was talking about confiscation, how they had confiscated thousands of pounds in cash hidden in shoe boxes at the Carters, and also very expensive jewellery. It was too soon to give the court a value but it appeared to be in the region of forty to fifty thousand pounds. He systematically went through each defendant, reading from a notebook what the police had found and taken.

A solicitor for Mr Dorfmann asked Clarke to verify a couple of points and so did David Edwards' solicitor. When it came to Matt, Mr Harvey stood up.

'Now we'll hear a thousand pounds worth of comments to justify his fee!'

'Detective Chief Inspector, there were eight police officers at the Davidsons' home. Three of them left the house to escort Mr Davidson to Bristol, and five officers stayed behind with Mrs Davidson and Mr Davidson's elderly mother. What exactly did they find at the Davidson house?'

'Nothing.'

'No jewellery?'

'No.'

'And no money?'

'No. As I've just said, nothing at all.'

Geoff observed that Harvey should have been a barrister and not a solicitor, as he was getting Clarke hot and bothered repeating his questions. I agreed he was very direct and to the point, which in court was very effective. Mr Harvey was getting into his stride.

'I believe one of your police officers took a letter from a file belonging to a client of Mr Davidson. This client's mother was living in Spain and had bought a small place in the sun as she was retired. The letter was referring to her and her property – a woman in her late sixties, nothing to do with this case at all. I'm sure you will agree, Chief Inspector, that compared to other defendants, the police found nothing of value to take away from Mr Davidson.'

'Well, he's used that piece of information I gave him to Matt's advantage,' I whispered to Geoff.

'That letter will be returned shortly,' said Clarke, not appearing to be quite so confident.

'Well, Chief Inspector, it's very interesting that Mr Davidson is in the middle of this case and you have absolutely nothing of evidence to show.'

'We believe we do have evidence against Mr Davidson.'

The magistrate said something to the clerk of the court, who promptly went over to the dock and whisked the defendants away as it was time to break for lunch. Matt seemed to disappear like the genie in Aladdin's lamp. If only Clarke could vanish in a puff of smoke never to be seen again!

Geoff walked out of the court and I followed.

'God, it's so horrible to hear a police officer speak complete lies about Matt. Come on, let's catch up with the motley crew heading towards the cafeteria sign. I'm sure the food won't be what we're used to, Geoff. We've lived such a charmed life after all, haven't we? One day Fortnum and Mason, another The Ritz, and now the icing on the cake, Le Petite Court Café.'

My poor attempt at a sarcastic joke fell flat as we walked into a very unloved-looking area with a few plastic tables and chairs, and a counter displaying unappealing sandwiches, muffins and a few chocolate bars. To be fair to the cafeteria staff, we could have been at Buckingham Palace waiting for a sumptuous meal and I would have hated it. We stood in a queue behind Jazmin Carter, who was in deep conversation with Jenny Thornton's mother.

'Hello, Claire, we were just wondering how come your Matt has got a nice suit on. We all brought cases of clean clothes and toiletries to the court first thing this morning, but we were told they weren't allowed, so we had to put them all in a locker.'

'We were told to come to Bristol last night, so we stayed over after I took Matt's clothes to the police station.'

This piece of information was met with silence. Obviously Jazmin thought her parents' solicitors should have told her the same, but I didn't want to get into who was right and who was wrong. It was wrong we were there in the first place.

I bought ham and cheese sandwiches, a coffee for Geoff and a safe mineral water for me, and we found a table by the window and sat with Jenny Thornton's mother, Pamela MacDonald. Adrienne Carter had told me casually one day that she had a very nice husband who worked somewhere in the City. Mrs MacDonald appeared very calm and reserved on the outside, and said she didn't have a clue why her daughter had been included. I said I felt the same about my husband.

Jazmin spent her time on her mobile and together with her relatives and the men we had seen earlier. We noticed them all leave and, looking out of the window, saw them all sitting on an outside wall. A couple of the men were smoking, and Jazmin was on her mobile again. Mrs MacDonald finished her coffee and said she would see us later as she was going to make a few calls.

'Now we've practically cleared the place out, you can tell me who Mrs MacDonald's daughter is and how she fits into the jigsaw.'

'I'll condense it, Geoff. There's only about another twenty minutes or so before we go back in, and I keep thinking about Matt. Where do they put defendants at lunchtime? Probably in some dingy court cell. I bet this place would seem like a five-star hotel to him right now! This is the most terrible experience to go through. I won't be happy until I see justice done.'

'Knowing you, I believe you completely, but I'm still waiting to hear about Jennifer Thornton!'

'We hardly know her. She's a friend of Mr and Mrs Carter. She's been a widow for about five years, I think. Her married name was Hirsch. Her husband Izzy used to be Matthew

Carter's right-hand man. Mr Carter never came to see Matt with his books and papers. They didn't even meet together at his home or ours. He was often away buying antiques, jewellery or paintings. Matt never asked because Izzy appeared to be very much involved in Mr Carter's working life. I think he was some sort of financial advisor, so he was able to understand the daily running of a company. Over the years he must have visited our home about two or maybe three times at the most, with bank statements and so on. He seemed pleasant, a small man, quite unassuming. I think he was of Israeli origin, but I could be wrong. He also had expertise in jewellery, so I think that was his working background. He said once that he helped Mr Carter choose jewellery for the auction houses, at least that's what we thought. We never had any reason to believe anything different. His demeanour wasn't threatening in any way, but at the same time neither was Matthew Carter's.'

'You said Jenny Thornton is a widow. Did her husband die of cancer or a heart attack?'

'No, he was shot outside his house, really horrible business! We were very shocked at the time, and the Carters were distraught. Jenny was left a young widow with a baby to bring up on her own.'

'It all sounds very Al Capone.'

'It's a mystery that has never been solved. We never thought for a moment that Matthew Carter was behind it. We actually felt very sorry for all of them; it must have been a horrible time, and they all coped admirably.'

'You are funny, Claire. For two intelligent people you were so naïve.'

'Maybe yes, maybe no. Who knows? You are like so many people who prefer to believe the bad about somebody rather than the good. I have always thought that if the police had one hundred per cent proof of who killed Mr Hirsch he or she would have been inside by now. I think there may have been a hidden agenda that we didn't know about, and after this week nothing would surprise me anymore. Anyway, Jenny Hirsch, or Thornton as she is now, tried to sort everything out. Her husband's death was obviously untimely, and he had left a load of paperwork for her to deal with. Together with Adrienne they did what they could to organize the bookkeeping. It wasn't easy for them, especially as Adrienne was breaking into acting and was busy reading scripts, meaning that Jenny was thrown in at the deep end. Matt and I had absolutely no idea of the ins and outs of how it was all run. Can you imagine how time-consuming it would be if Matt questioned all his clients in an in-depth way? They would probably tell him to go to hell anyway. Accountants can only advise and even if they get as far as taking a client to the well, they can't make them drink. Anyway she helped out for a while and then, as you know, in 2000 I became very ill. At the beginning of 2001 we had our first visit from the National Crime Squad. It's all pretty intriguing.'

6

Outside the court room it was busier than ever. Apparently there was a half-hour delay for whatever reason and it seemed as though family and friends had grown in number around Jazmin. Four of Clarke's cronies were sitting together but there wasn't any sign of Neil Harvey. He and the other solicitors were probably in the court with Clarke and the prosecution. I sat next to a man who had all the signs of being a member of Clarke's fraternity: stone-coloured raincoat, flat feet, and similar mannerisms, even down to the tone of his voice. The only difference was that he was quite tall and fairly slim, whereas Clarke stocky. They definitely came from the same charm school. I thought it was strange that none of the arresting police officers were at the court. It was as though they had been told to keep away.

I whispered to Geoff, 'I wonder if it's compulsory on their CV to look bland and boring? I despise the lot of them.'

'That's obvious by the look on your face. I can understand how you feel, though. Matt is being used by the system and you feel helpless.'

I phoned Sam and Helen, but as I had nothing to tell them I fluffed my lines and promised I would call as soon as I knew what was happening. At 2.30 we were allowed in. There was Matt back in the middle of the dock, still not looking towards us. It was quite unbearable. All the solicitors were chatting together in the centre of the court, papers were being shuffled, the magistrate was in deep conversation with the court clerk and we just sat there like puppets waiting for someone to pull the strings.

Jennifer Thornton's solicitor stood up and addressed the magistrate. 'Sir, my client is a widow with a child who is six years old, so please would the court take this into consideration as Ms Thornton has never been away from her daughter before.' He added, 'Ms Thornton's mother is a JP and bail monies are not an issue.'

Neil Harvey came over and said, 'Mr and Mrs Carter are not going for bail, they know they are being kept in custody for a while, but the other defendants are. Will you go on the stand for Matt?'

'Of course, I will.'

'Good. This is the procedure: Ms Thornton's mother is going first, then Mr Dorfmann's wife followed by Mr Edwards' partner and finally you. And, by the way, I have read Paul's faxed letter and given a copy to the magistrate. At the first opportunity I shall read it out loud to the court. It's very well written so hopefully will help.'

I looked at the crowded court. It was all very false: on one side there was the glass dock lumping everyone together, while Mr Totally Innocent waited for someone to help him; and opposite the National Crime Squad, grinning and laughing with the CPS solicitor. I can't really put into words how I felt; it was all so unreal. Not our typical Friday afternoon, that's for sure! I felt hemmed in and knew I had to get some air for a minute. I asked Geoff to listen in case anything of value was said in Matt's favour. The one time I left the court, Neil Harvey decided to read out Paul's letter.

'I have to say, Harvey can teach the prosecuting solicitor a trick or two on how to read out loud. He did Paul's words justice. Bloody good letter, Claire, shame you missed it.'

'Thanks for rubbing that in, Geoff! Typical of me.'

Pamela MacDonald took the oath and spoke very eloquently. She reiterated what her daughter's solicitor had said about her young granddaughter Alice, and said she would have no problem putting up surety. She certainly didn't want her daughter to languish in a cell when monies could be found almost immediately. The figure quoted to her was so high, more than half a million pounds, I began to feel faint! Mrs Dorfmann was next. I had never seen her before and I knew that Matt hadn't either. She ranted on about their house being worth a million pounds but she emphasized that it was heavily mortgaged. Still, she felt confident she could raise whatever monies were needed. A similar scenario was played out with Dave Edwards' girlfriend, who said she could get hold of three to four hundred thousand pounds.

Geoff kept saying, 'Bloody disgraceful!' And I felt as though we weren't in a court room at all, that perhaps I was dreaming and we were really bidding for a Ming vase. Except of course that we were bidding for people's lives and, more importantly to me, my husband's liberty.

'Mrs Davidson please.'

I took my oath and went on the stand, which was right in front of DCI Clarke and his comrades. They were literally touching distance from me, not that I wanted to touch them, but I fixed my gaze on Clarke's toad-like face. As Matt's representative in court, Neil Harvey had to direct the questions to me.

'Mrs Davidson, how would you describe your husband?'

'He's a wonderful family man. He has the utmost integrity. He's never, ever been in any sort of trouble in his life. He's never done anything wrong other than supporting West Ham United, and eating too much pasta and too many wine gums!'

I didn't expect to get the reaction I received, but most people laughed. Even the magistrate smiled and I saw a faint grin from Matt.

'Mrs Davidson, do you think, if granted bail, your husband would abscond?'

'That is an absolutely outrageous question and my answer is "Here is his passport."'

I handed it to the clerk. When I think back I really didn't know why I'd brought Matt's passport. I'd just seen it in a drawer and something guided me to bring it to the court.

'One more question, Mrs Davidson. Can you raise surety for your husband?'

I answered yes, although I didn't have a clue if I could or not. But I was going to bloody well try.

'Thank you, Mrs Davidson. You may step down.'

Another break was announced for ten minutes, probably whilst the magistrate had a cup of tea. A middle-aged man, one of the solicitors who seemed to have a rare sense of humour, came over and introduced himself as Matthew Carter's solicitor Gerald Harris.

'You were extremely good on the stand, very funny and straightforward. You should be a professional witness for defendants. I shall dine on your comments for quite a while.'

'I'm glad you found it all so amusing!' I silently thanked my mother for having sent me as a child to elocution and drama classes. She used to say it was very good grounding, and she was right. I had grown up never to be afraid to speak up, and to have confidence in myself and positive belief. If I was a crumbling wreck inside, no one would ever know. Just one more thing, Mum: could you, Dad and my father-in-law please sprinkle some after-life magic into these proceedings and free Matt?

Mr Harvey came over and said, 'Well done, I think the magistrate actually showed he had teeth for once! We need to sort out surety as time is getting on, and I didn't ask you on the stand a surety amount. Can you raise two hundred thousand in surety and fifteen thousand in cash?'

I was stunned. I knew I had to get bail monies, but in Matt's case I thought it would be in the region of twenty-five thousand. Don't ask me why I thought that amount, I suppose I really didn't have a clue, but the amount Neil Harvey was suggesting via the magistrate was impossible. Off the top of my head I couldn't think of people who could find that magic number – oil millionaires were not in our address book – so I just blurted out, 'The figures are too high. I may be able to get a hundred thousand surety and five thousand in cash?'

Mr Harvey checked with the clerk and came back almost immediately with a positive 'Yes, that amount is fine. Can you go and make your phone calls to friends, and see if you can get surety sorted with names and addresses for the court so it can be expedited?'

I was given fifteen minutes to arrange whatever I could. I went into the corridor and first of all rang Carol and Mike. True to their word they were in and waiting for my call. I explained it was for surety and that I had been asked to raise two hundred thousand but had managed to bring it down to a hundred thousand. Whatever anyone could pledge in shares or bonds I knew Matt would appreciate one hundred per cent. I think I must have held my breath in anticipation of perhaps a negative answer. Let's face it, I was asking for help 'big time' and even if people want to help, it doesn't always work out that they are able to.

Carol immediately said she could help with sixty thousand in shares, and obviously Mike was in full agreement. If technology was such that I could have hugged and kissed them through the phone I would have done it on the spot. What wonderful friends! Matt and I would never forget it. I thanked them both with all my heart and then telephoned Paul.

I was fortunate that he had just come out of a court hearing and didn't have his mobile switched off. He said he had spoken to Miri about Matt and that she was absolutely amazed someone like Matt could be in such a terrible situation. He said they both agreed that ten thousand could be put in, and that he would be in court after the May holiday weekend, so would swear it in on Tuesday morning. I thanked him and promised to phone him over the weekend. So, seventy thousand was in place. I rang my mother-in-law last and explained the amount needed. She said her sister Laura had bonds to the value of thirty thousand pounds, and that as it wasn't cash it wouldn't be encroaching on her lifestyle. She said it was a pledge that everyone had faith in Matt being honourable, and that hopefully, sooner rather than later, the documentation would be put in a file marked 'Case Closed'. I told Helen to thank Laura and said I felt quite positive that Matt would be coming home with us. Again, what did I know? But I rang off feeling more hopeful. I had been told by Mr Harvey that as five thousand cash wasn't such an important pledge I could sort it out at the weekend and let him know. So that worry I could put on a back burner for the present.

I went back into the court room and handed the names and addresses to Mr Harvey. Geoff informed me he had been speaking to Gerald Harris, who told him I shouldn't worry and that Matt would definitely be freed. There was no doubt about it, though in his opinion not yet. Possibly in a couple of weeks...

'What? How has he come to that conclusion?' I looked across at Matt who was now staring upwards to the ceiling. 'This is stomach-churning stuff. Stupid bloody solicitor, why should he care how many weeks an innocent person languishes in prison?'

The magistrate had been given all the addresses in connection with the surety. He first referred to Mr and Mrs Carter, saying that bail wasn't on the agenda, and within seconds they had been taken away. The same happened to Brian Dorfmann and David Edwards, who also weren't granted bail. At this point I felt sick and dug my fingernails into Geoff's hand.

'I will grant bail to both Jennifer Thornton and Matt Davidson, but because it's late, almost 5.30 on a Friday, plus it's a Bank Holiday weekend, nothing can be sworn in until next Tuesday 6th May at the earliest.'

I only heard bail had been granted for Matt and didn't take in the rest. In my muddled state all I saw was Jenny Thornton and my husband being escorted out of the dock. I hadn't actually grasped the reality that Matt couldn't be free until all shares and cash were lodged into various courts, and I barely knew what day it was. The Bank Holiday Monday significance was lost on me, so when realization dawned that Matt would be staying locked up for the next few days I couldn't think straight.

All the solicitors were packing their briefcases. Mr Harris waved goodbye and said, 'Good luck. I'm sure Matt will be home quicker than I originally thought, but not quick enough for you, of course.'

I mumbled 'Thank you' and stopped Neil Harvey in his tracks as he seemed to be rushing with other colleagues to catch a train to London. 'Could you please tell me where Matt is? Can I see him as I don't understand the procedure?'

'No, I'm afraid you're not allowed, but I'll see if I can have a quick word and get back to you.'

'Listen, Geoff, I'm going to tell Samantha a condensed version of events and please stick with it. The same will be for Helen.' Geoff nodded in agreement.

I phoned my daughter to say we were ready to leave and would explain when we saw her. She was already waiting outside, having expected us to be on our way out. I couldn't wait to get out of the horrible place. Sam looked very vulnerable standing on her own. I gave her a massive hug and told her briefly, 'Although Dad has been granted his freedom, we have to be patient and wait for the blasted Bank Holiday weekend to finish before Carol can pledge sixty thousand shares, Paul ten grand and Aunt Laura thirty thousand in bonds. On top of all this, the court wants five thousand in cash, which I have to hand-deliver on Tuesday.'

'So where have they taken Dad?'

'I'm not sure, but he's on remand so it's probably a place with relaxed rules, and perhaps somewhere in the countryside. Mr Harvey is supposed to be seeing Dad for a moment and I would like to wait and see what he says. Unfortunately we are not allowed to see Dad tonight, but I'll sort something out over the weekend. Look, Jazmin Carter is over there with her aunt and uncle. Her parents have been taken into custody for a while and I feel sorry for her, regardless of what's happened to Dad. Do you think you could say hello to her? I know you would rather not, but you're bigger and better than that.'

Sam is a warm, compassionate and caring individual and she went over and gave Jazmin a cuddle. I believe Jazmin with her bravado told Sam, 'Matt will be home very soon and the police will have egg on their faces.' These few words encouraged our daughter very slightly.

Mr Harvey came running out to grab a cab with two other solicitors. I ran and asked him, 'Have you seen my husband?'

He replied, 'Only for a split second before he was taken to prison.'

'Where is he?'

'I'm not sure, but I will get back to you. Have a safe journey home.' And he was gone.

Sam had gone on ahead to her car, so I said this just to Geoff. I rang my mother-in-law and told her briefly that only three of us were coming home for dinner, as Matt had to wait until after the Bank Holiday. I reassured her that he wouldn't be staying in a terrible place, and told her I would explain when we were home.

Geoff sat next to Sam in the car. They talked about her day and he told her snippets of ours. Sitting in the back I tried to collect my thoughts. Even as I write this now I find it hard to express how many different emotions I was trying to deal with. How can people who have a powerful role to play believe their power can be used to inflict pain? The law seems to have a licence to enable bullies to dish out punishment just to suit them. Why? Where am I living? How many good, innocent men and women find themselves in a similar situation to Matt? I realized there must be many, but when you live your daily life in a fairly unspectacular fashion how many of us realize what really goes on beyond our own small world? I kept wondering where they had taken Matt and whether he was all right. On paper now it doesn't look as scary as it felt then. I also had the feeling we were a long way off from living our lives again in the way we'd been used to. There was definitely far more to this case than we had seen yet.

7

After the long drive home I wasn't surprised to see how strained and tired Helen looked. I'm not sure what is worse, waiting by the phone for news or actually being at the court and seeing the agony first hand. I don't think there's a great deal to choose from. Even though Helen appeared tired, she had cooked a three-course meal for us. I know if I had been in her position I would have spent my day pacing the floor, drinking endless cups of coffee and going crazy, and the evening meal would have been a takeaway of some description. Unfortunately Sam and I couldn't do Helen's supper justice and we just picked at the meal, letting Geoff be the one to enjoy my mother-in-law's excellent home baking skills.

Geoff had parked his bike on our drive, and as soon as he had finished eating he thought it best to go home, as by the time he had put on his biking paraphernalia it would be quite late and he didn't like driving across London at the best of times during the day, let alone at night. I never thought he was happy and comfortable on his bike.

Sam went to bed before midnight. She must have felt completely done in, both mentally and physically. The drive alone is tiring, but the lack of a positive result made it worse. Sadly it all hung in the balance. Helen also went to bed, but I made and received some phone calls from those few people who had heard about Matt. One call from Susan, a family friend, asked if there was anything she and her husband Derek could do to help. I really appreciated the thought but told her that, other than freeing my husband and changing the judicial system for the better overnight, there was nothing I needed. Still, her enquiry into our wellbeing was enough to try and keep us going.

I sat up once again through the night with my new best friend the brandy bottle. I was in the same pattern as before: very little sleep. But I couldn't rest, so I was raring to go by 7.30 a.m. and itching to telephone Neil Harvey, although I knew I couldn't phone him on a Saturday morning before 9. Helen had a hairdresser's appointment every Saturday and I felt it was important for her to go as usual, just to lift her morale and hopefully make her feel a little better.

By 8.45 I couldn't wait any longer and I phoned Mr Harvey. I wasn't any good at playing the little wife at home waiting game! He answered almost immediately and said he knew it would be me ringing. I apologised as I could hear it was a family breakfast, with children laughing in the background.

'Can you please tell me where my husband is?'

His tone was the same as ever, offhand and impersonal. 'I have no idea! Your husband was taken away too quickly for me to ascertain his whereabouts.'

'What do you suggest I do now, then?'

'Ring the court and ask them. They'll tell you.'

'I'll do that, Mr Harvey. Your cheque will be posted to you today. How much do we actually owe you, considering you stayed overnight in a hotel and had to take taxis back and forth to the police station?'

'It's still a thousand pounds. You are a friend of Paul's and that's the amount I said originally. I'll be in touch after the Bank Holiday.'

'On Tuesday I'm going back to Bristol to lodge five thousand pounds in cash. Hopefully the shares and bonds will have been put into various courts, so I'll speak to you then, Mr Harvey. Have a good weekend.'

I rang off, wondering how he could not have any idea

where Matt was. I rang Directory Enquiries and asked for the Bristol magistrates' court. I was put through almost immediately, but was met with a recorded answer phone message: 'This court is now closed for the May Bank Holiday weekend. The court will re-open at 9 a.m. on Tuesday 6th May. Goodbye.'

I had actually thought it weird that Harvey recommended me phoning the court in the first place, as I didn't think there would be any admin staff there on a Saturday morning. Harvey must have been in a court hundreds of times and known they wouldn't be open on a normal Saturday, let alone a Bank Holiday. I sat and thought about who I should be phoning – obviously not Harvey, he wasn't at all interested in us! I glanced at the notes I had written in Bristol – as a writer I was always putting pen to paper – and I saw I had written down the telephone number of the dreaded police station in Bristol where Matt had been detained. I prayed they weren't all on a weekend break, but, thank goodness, a man answered very quickly. I thought I recognized his voice as the one and only friendly, human policeman I had seen at the station on Thursday night. I told him my name and mentioned Matt, and he said he remembered him. I asked if he had any idea where they had put Matt on remand until the surety was in place. To my surprise he said there was only one prison there, called Horfield. I remember sounding dumbfounded.

'Only one prison? Is it an open one?'

'No, Mrs Davidson, it's an A1 security prison.'

'Oh my God, how can they put my husband in such a terrible place?'

'He's on remand, Mrs Davidson; he'll be put in a separate wing. Don't worry, he's a nice man and he'll be all right. They will look after him.'

'I sincerely hope so. Do you have a number for this Horfield prison, please?'

'Yes, and may I suggest you ring them right away and

explain you live in London and you need a pass or passes for a visit. Unfortunately they get very busy, so do it quickly, and good luck for the future.'

I thanked him for the number and the help that I knew I should have automatically received from the solicitor. I was surprised that he did not seem to know where Matt was and it seemed from his tone as if he just wanted an easy life instead of grief from me. Well, I'd give the whole bloody judicial service grief until I got my husband away from them.

I immediately telephoned Horfield and explained that I didn't know the procedure, or how things worked, but could I please have three passes to visit Matt. The person at the other end of the phone sounded as warm and helpful as the policeman did. Was it possible I was speaking to another kind person? And this time one working in a high grade prison?

He said, 'It's too late to visit today. All the passes have been allocated, and no one is allowed to visit the prison on a Sunday, but you can all visit on Bank Holiday Monday. The visiting times are 2 p.m. until 2.45, and you must be here thirty minutes before as there is always a queue.'

I gave him our names and he said our passes would be ready to collect on our way in. I thanked him for being so informative and rang off. Am I now officially a prisoner's wife? Is Sam a prisoner's daughter? And perhaps even more poignantly, is Helen a prisoner's mother? We have gone from one relaxed Saturday to the following Saturday through what can only be described as living hell!

With my mother-in-law still at the hairdresser's and Sam needing her well-earned rest in bed, I wrote a list of names of people I could phone to ask if they could help us. I only had three days to raise five thousand pounds and I thought that if a few people could put whatever they could afford into the kitty, then once I had lodged the amount on Tuesday I could see if Helen and I could think of someone else who could

69

afford to help us pay everyone back quickly. It was such a horrible thing to do. I plucked up the courage, phoned Kate and told her the truth. After explaining to her that Matt hadn't been ill but had been arrested, her reaction was the same as everyone else's. I explained the sorry saga and she immediately said, 'No problem. Ask Sam if she can come over to the hotel later today and I'll give her five hundred pounds. I speak for Keith as well, as I know he won't mind.'

'Thank you, Kate. I promise you'll get it back in a few days.'

After Kate I phoned Geoff and told him about the morning's phone calls. He said if we only needed money for a few days, then he could get two and a half thousand in cash and could bring it over that day. He said he wouldn't be able to stay long as he was visiting a niece. Thanking him, I carried on with my calls. After just a few the five thousand, albeit temporarily, was in place.

By the time Helen came home from the hairdresser's, Sam was dressed and eating a late breakfast. I knew I couldn't put off the true facts any longer.

'I have to explain to you both that although Dad is on remand, as I said yesterday, I have made various calls this morning and found out there is only one prison in Bristol and it's an A1 grade security one. Before you say anything, I can see how shocked you both look, but I have been assured that he isn't stuck with murderers. They have put him in a different wing as he'll be out in a few days. I've organized three passes to visit him on Monday. I know you want to go, but are you sure you can handle this, Helen?'

'Of course; he's my son.'

'And what about you Sam? Are you able to face it?'

'I'll make myself. I want to see Dad.'

'I understand, and I wish I could magically change everything right now, but if we stick together as a team we'll all get through this.'

'Is there anything I can do, Mum, to help this weekend? I need to keep occupied.'

'Well, I have to lodge five thousand pounds in cash at Bristol magistrates' court on Tuesday. It will expedite Dad's freedom, but it's on top of the shares and bonds. It's awful, a disgraceful money racket around someone's pain and misery. Before I put on my thinking cap and magically pull out of a hat one person who can stick five grand into the pot without it making a big hole in their pockets, I've had to ring round to various friends to ask them to donate whatever they can into the kitty. I have telephoned Kate and Keith and told Kate the truth. She was very sympathetic and said if you go to the hotel tonight they will be happy to help with five hundred. But I think you have done a great deal of driving so I will go tomorrow by train and collect it.'

'Mum! You look very tired too, and I just offered to help! He's my Dad and I love him.'

'Are you sure you don't mind driving all that way today, after your drive to Bristol and back yesterday? I'm sure Kate and Keith won't mind if you want to stay overnight at the hotel and come home tomorrow.'

'No thanks, Mum, I'd rather go there, see Kate and Keith for a while and drive back late tonight. I'm seeing a few friends tomorrow in Hampstead so it's better for me, and gives me a chance to unwind before I drive to Bristol on Monday.'

'Thanks darling, that's such a great help.'

'Don't be ridiculous! I'll help as much as I can. I'm just going to make a couple of calls and sort some things out in my room.'

About five minutes later, Sam came running downstairs with her jacket on, car keys in her hand. 'Okay both of you, I'm going to pick up Amy. She's offered to come with me to Bournemouth; you know how lovely she is. She doesn't blab and gossip and she likes you and Dad, so she will be good company for me.'

'I'm really pleased she's going with you. I've always liked her; she's beautiful inside and out and a good friend that you can speak your mind to. Drive safely and let us know when you are there please.'

Sam gave her grandmother a kiss and Helen as usual stood there all stiff and starchy, not because she was a cold person, she wasn't! She was, however, useless when it came to the touchy, feely stuff. Me – I'm very tactile so I enveloped Sam in a bear hug and watched her manoeuvre her car with expertise out of the drive.

Alone with Helen I explained in more detail about the morning's calls. 'I know you're as worried as I am. The thought of some murdering lunatic giving Matt a hard time is making me feel ill, so God knows what it's doing to your stomach! I hope the prison officers look after him. He hasn't been convicted of anything, so fingers crossed he isn't sharing a cell with a lookalike from *The Silence of the Lambs.* Sorry to be so blunt about it all. I have tried to keep as much as possible from you, but as we are going to see him on Monday it seems pointless trying to hide the truth.'

'I can't believe my son is going through such a terrible ordeal. So much for British justice! I wonder if he will phone us today or even if he's allowed to? We can't phone him.'

We sat and talked about the situation, and at about 5 p.m. Matt phoned us. I was so happy and relieved to hear his voice, but I could tell he was trying not to be emotional as his voice cracked. I told him the first thing that came into my head, in what I hope was a well-disguised upbeat voice. 'Everyone cries when they speak to me! The three of us are coming to see you on Monday as there are no visitors allowed on a Sunday. I promise you it will all be sorted out on Tuesday.'

He seemed to cheer up a little, although he couldn't be on the phone long, and he actually came to life for a moment when I told him the magic words that West Ham had won that day! I sent him all our love and he sent it back, but I put the phone down feeling completely lost. I tried to cover up, because it wasn't just me in this; there was Helen and Samantha to consider, and of course Matt himself! I would be no good to anyone if I crumbled, so I talked to Helen about what to do financially, who we should ask to help us with the five thousand pounds. I knew we really needed it by Tuesday, as although people were being more than kind and helpful towards us, they all needed their money back quickly. We discussed it at length trying to decide the best way forward and crossing people's names off the list I had scribbled out.

'He's no good, not at all approachable.'

'She's very difficult, and would never understand why Matt was in such a terrible place.'

'He's not right: he would want it back within a week. What would we do if the court kept it longer than that? We would have an added headache, that's for sure.'

We both agreed we would speak to Helen's sister-in-law Bertha. I called her Bertie. She was a lovely lady, always immaculate in her clothes, hair and make-up, and I admired her enormously. Before Bertie married into Helen's family she had been briefly married during the war. She hardly spoke about her first husband, as he had left her life as swiftly as he had come into it. But they had a child, a daughter Marilyn, who sadly lived in a nursing home as she had been ill for a long time, and over the years her condition had been getting worse. We explained to Bertha what had happened to Matt and naturally she uttered the same words as everyone else. I told her about the one hundred thousand pound surety, plus the cash I had to lodge in Bristol Crown Court on Tuesday. I said we had considered asking a very old uncle of Helen's; he was a widower without any children, but he could be extremely difficult and we were only thinking of him as a last resort, as we both felt very loath to go and see him. Bertie told us not to even consider it for a second. Sadly Marilyn wasn't able to go out to restaurants, clubs or shopping on her own, but there was money put aside for her, as Bertie's wealthy brother had set up a trust fund and put monies into a current account for the sole purpose that Bertie could look after her daughter without any financial strain on her purse. Therefore, although it had all been written up in a will and was legally binding, Bertie was allowed to take money out at her own discretion, as long as it was a loan and would be given back to Marilyn.

'Claire! Don't go to anyone else! You don't know how long you are going to need five thousand pounds for! Let's hope for Matt's sake it will be very quick, but, as we don't know the law and have never encountered anything like this before, the court may keep the cash for a while. This way, Marilyn can benefit from any interest made on it. It's not a problem for me at all. I will get it for you first thing on Tuesday morning.'

We couldn't thank her enough.

8

By Bank Holiday Monday everything had fallen into place. I had a list of names ready for the 'Free Matt Fund' and had promised all those involved that their donations would only be needed if Bertie's money wasn't going to be in place by Tuesday, but even then all the cash would be returned just after the weekend.

Sam was ready at 9 a.m. She had spent Sunday with friends and had a fresh spurt of vitality, which was more than you could say for Helen and me, though we did our best to look cheerful. The weather for once was good for a Bank Holiday, and we looked like a typical family going out for the day to enjoy ourselves. Little did the neighbours know where we were really going! And even if they did, they probably wouldn't have commented or understood. Many of the houses had gone 'buy to let', and nobody knew much about their neighbours.

Sam is a very good, competent driver and, because we had left London early, we missed the build-up of holiday traffic. By 11.30 a.m. a sign for Horfield outside Bristol showed it was only a few miles away. We all agreed to try and find the prison first, so we could get our bearings and see if it was easy to park. Once we had done that, we'd maybe go for a walk and stop at a country pub or a quaint tea room to eat lunch.

It will probably sound crazy when you read this, but the three of us had no idea what to expect from an A1 grade security prison, and we definitely weren't prepared for the sight that appeared to block the sun in front of us. The highest walls we had ever seen seemed to stretch on forever. We all fell silent as Sam parked opposite the beginning of the 'Great Wall of Horfield'. We walked to the entrance area, which was just as intimidating, with massive black doors that didn't need the words 'Keep Out' written across them. Just the look of the place made you want to run.

Through our horror and sheer disbelief my mobile rang. I remember we all jumped at the same time. I think I must have sounded most peculiar to a very good friend of mine who had been away and didn't know about Matt. At that moment, I didn't want to try and explain it to her, so I mumbled my way through the most inane conversation, hopefully without sounding extremely rude, and made an excuse to ring off.

We went back to the car and sat there staring in a bewildered state, as the scenery facing us showed us a very negative picture.

'Somewhere behind those grotty walls is Dad! I want to kill someone for doing this!'

'Me too, and then where would we be? Behind similar walls. I think we should leave the car here. There isn't a restriction for a change, plus we have Nana's disability badge. Let's get away from the prison for the moment and find somewhere to have a sandwich. Aren't you both hungry?'

'No, not at all,' they both said together.

'No, neither am I. So let's just go for a walk.'

Walking in silence can sometimes feel companionable, if you are thinking happy thoughts or simply enjoying the lovely surroundings wherever you happen to be. In our case we were all so miserable, angry and frustrated that someone as kind, gentle and caring as Matt could be thrown into the lion's den in this way that it wouldn't have made any difference if we'd been walking in the gardens of a wonderful stately home or in a rat-infested alleyway. We wouldn't have noticed. I feel sure that people who have gone through a similar experience will fully understand. We didn't walk very far because it wasn't good for Helen. She suffers with asthma and, at her age, we didn't want her to have breathing difficulties if we could help it. We also didn't want to lose our bearings as the visit wasn't long in the first place and we didn't want to arrive late.

The local area wasn't picturesque, in the way of the fictional village where Agatha Christie's Miss Marple character lived. I suppose you wouldn't realistically find pretty thatched cottages by the side of a country pub with a typical English flower garden and tables and chairs giving everyone a wonderful view of a bloody prison. No, I have visited Bristol many times – it's a beautiful city and the countryside is lovely – but wherever there's a prison it's dire!

We may not have been hungry, but we did need a hot drink. We found a café about five minutes away, though as it was so local the other customers were all prison officers. The three of us felt like fishes out of water. We found a table in a corner and Sam scowled whenever a prison officer came in. They all had keys jangling on their belts and some of the women reminded me of Anne, the policewoman who had come to our flat in 2001.

'I suppose, if you are able to do the kind of work they do, you harden yourself to the task in hand. Let's face it, it's one hell of a job! You couldn't employ a sweet, soft-natured person to keep hard-nosed criminals in line.'

'Yes, I agree, but Dad's not one! So what is he doing in such a crappy place?'

We sat there for an age, making our drinks last.

'Okay, it's gone 1 p.m. Let's go back and see if there's a queue.'

As the prison came into view we could see there was a line forming.

'Obviously these are local people and they sadly know the ropes.'

We stood behind women who had brought their children to see maybe daddy, and some of them looked lifeless as if the visits were all they had to cling on to. I felt very sad for them and us. Helen, Sam and I must have looked very uncomfortable standing there. We didn't dress in designer clothes, none of us own any Armani or similar, but we must have looked like novices. One woman asked whether we had been there before. I told her no and she said, 'It's not as bad as it looks. Some of the officers are all right, and you get used to the others who need to scream and shout!'

I wanted to say 'We will never get used to it!' But it sounded very heartless and pompous, and I didn't want to appear unfriendly. I didn't want to ask her any questions, though, about who she was visiting. I didn't want her to question us in return.

At 1.30 the doors opened. We slowly moved forward as everyone's names were checked and passes shown. It took a long time because the officers at the desk were friendly with frequent visitors whom they knew quite well. When we, the alien three, arrived at the desk, before we could say anything, the desk officer looked at us and commented, 'Are you sure you're in the right place?'

I immediately answered, 'No, we're not! But neither should Matt Davidson be here.'

'Oh yes,' came the reply. 'I know who he is. He came in on Friday night, nice man from London. Have you come that far as well?'

'Yes, we have.'

'Well, the statistics show that approximately four thousand prisoners in British prisons shouldn't be inside.'

I think we all looked dazed and I said, 'That's terrible. So much for justice in this country.'

'Well, I take it you're Mrs Davidson? Don't look so worried. He'll be out shortly and he's okay. Now, here's a key as you have to put your mobile and any valuables into a locker behind you, and here's a ticket you can all share. Once you've done that go to the X-ray machine where they'll check your handbags and so on. Looking at you I shouldn't think you'll need the full usual routine but that's the rules, I'm afraid.'

I thanked him for his help and with some much needed humour I said, 'Please take this in the nicest possible way: we all hope we don't see you again!'

'Well, he at least seemed very personable,' said Helen, as the officer smiled at us, making her at least feel a little better.

'Yes, he seems much nicer than the café mob we saw before.'

We did as we were told and watched as women and men were degraded in front of us. Not quite the same airport ritual that you would expect at Heathrow or Gatwick! I looked at Helen's face as she tried to understand why people had to have their hair and mouth checked.

'Ugh! How horrible! It looks like they are checking the hair for nits.'

'No, Helen, I doubt it. It's to do with drugs.'

The three of us must have looked pretty soft, nerdy types, thank goodness, as when it came to our turn they glossed over us very briefly. Maybe it was the thought of putting their plastic-gloved hands into my mother-in-law's mouth and pulling out her new shiny false teeth that happily put them off. Whatever the reason, we got over that hurdle without too much fuss.

Hurdle number two stared at us almost immediately as we dutifully followed everyone up a staircase that had the welcome sign waiting at the top. A prison officer was standing with man's best friend, a lovely, cuddly German shepherd dog who looked as though any minute he would roll over and let you give him a tummy rub. I don't think so! Someone in front of us noticed our reticence in walking past him.

'He's a sniffer dog, so, unless you're bringing in a load of drugs that the X-ray machine failed to see, you have nothing to worry about.'

'Christ! This will be a visit we'll never forget.'

Turning a corner we came into a very large area with tables and chairs spread across the room. I noticed when we sat down at a table with four chairs that three of them were in the same colour and the fourth chair was a completely different shade. It spelt out 'prisoner's chair'. How pathetic! What happened to prisoners who sat in a visitor's chair by mistake? One hundred lines, one hundred lashes or even solitary confinement! It was almost 2 p.m. I thought I would go to the snack counter and buy tea and chocolate bars. Sitting waiting for Matt to arrive was very daunting; we didn't know what to expect. The tables were spaced a few feet apart from each other so that people couldn't hear each other's conversation. I looked across at the table nearest to us and thought I recognized the man sitting on his own, possibly waiting for Matthew Carter. I felt sure he had sat opposite Geoff and me at the wonderful waiting area at the court on Friday, and was a friend of the Carter family.

At the back of the meeting hall or makeshift cafeteria, a sudden rush of men from all walks of life came in. Matt came towards us and in his own inimitable fashion immediately mouthed 'I'm all right' and smiled: typical of Matt! He may have felt absolutely traumatized, but he wouldn't show it to us. Sam grabbed him first and hugged him and then Helen and I managed to get a look-in. I was relieved to see that he was actually in an upbeat mood. His quite good spirits meant that, unless he was an extremely good actor, he was dealing with the situation very well. He even made a joke about the wonderful bright orange-coloured bibs that all inmates wore to distinguish them from the visitors. Sitting directly behind Matt was Mathew Carter with the man I'd noticed before. Mr Carter looked across at me and said 'I'm sorry'. I shrugged and tried to smile.

'Who are you smiling at Mum?'

'Matthew Carter is sitting behind us with a visitor and as he acknowledged me I returned the acknowledgement.'

Before Sam could respond, Matt said, 'Look, we don't have much time together, but don't be angry with him. He's looked after me and I really don't blame him. I blame bloody Clarke.'

Rather than get into an in-depth and heavy conversation, we changed the subject and talked about his football team doing well for a change! Matt told us about his room mate. Apparently his teeth had been professionally whitened to such an extent that they glowed pearly white, and Matt was sure he could have shaved in front of them as they would have been a good substitute for a magnifying mirror.

'Talking about more serious things, what's happening tomorrow, Claire?'

'Laura and Leslie are coming with me tomorrow. The idea is for me to lodge Bertha's cash at good old Bristol magistrates court, Laura can pledge her bonds and, hey presto, with a bit of luck you will be coming home with us. Otherwise I shall bring a load of sheets tied together and you can act like the male Rapunzel and climb out of your room or cell and make your escape! Actually, joking aside Matt, I feel very confident tomorrow will be fine. Paul is going to be working in court tomorrow and will be able to do it there. Carol is going to a court in Hertfordshire, so keep your fingers crossed.'

Forty-five minutes isn't very long and the visit was soon over. We watched him go and I think we all felt gutted at leaving him. We collected our belongings from the locker and drove away from the wall, hoping that by the same time tomorrow Matt would have left that place forever.

'Dad put on such a brave act, bless him. He obviously didn't want us to see him looking depressed. How can the authorities treat Dad and others like him in such an atrocious way? It's bloody disgusting in that prison.'

'Sam, did you expect a prison to be on a par with The Ritz?

We have no idea about the machinations surrounding the British law system or lack of it! How often are we in trouble? Sadly, for some people this is a daily occurrence, but to us it's a horror story and something we've never had to think about before. This has completely opened my eyes to at least understanding there's a massive problem within the law, but let's get Dad out of there and then we can try and deal with all the grey, hidden issues. Nothing is simply black and white. At least Dad had humour and left us in good spirits, even if it was a brilliantly rehearsed act.'

Helen looked a little more hopeful. 'I agree, Claire, it wasn't as bad as I thought it would be. When I saw the entrance to the prison I was dreading it! But the worst part is the rigmarole that everyone has to go through: ears and mouth checked, hair inspected. Not every prisoner, as we can vouch first-hand, is a criminal and the same goes for their visitors. I noticed some of the wives and their children looked so sad. It's a different world altogether.'

That night we all went to bed in a positive frame of mind. Tuesday would be a good day.

Bertie kept to her word, and before 9.30 a.m. Tuesday morning she came over with cash in an envelope.

'I would never get up this early normally, but as this is an emergency and I hope it really helps Matt I was the first customer in the bank at 9 a.m.'

'Thank you so much. Just to safeguard everything I have typed a note for us both to sign stating that the monies belong to Marilyn and will be paid back to her with possibly some interest. If you want me to add anything tell me.'

'It's fine, Claire. Here you are, I've signed it. Now you go and get your husband back.'

'Talking about husbands, where's Uncle Harry?'

'He's sitting in the car doing his crossword, as sociable as ever! I think Laura and Leslie have arrived and they are talking to happy Harry now!'

Helen came in from the garden. She enjoyed pottering around out there, it relaxed her. Bertie stayed another five minutes talking to Helen, and between Laura, Leslie and I, we all made a promise that Matt would come back today, a promise that was out of our hands.

I was beginning to know the route very well. Uncle Leslie enjoyed driving and was a calm and careful driver. Arriving at the NCP in Nelson Street opposite the magistrates' court seemed surreal.

'Maybe we'll be lucky, Claire, and have it all sorted before lunch. Then we can meet Matt early.'

'I would love to believe that, Laura, but this is England and just after the Bank Holiday. I doubt if anyone is even in yet!'

Unhappily, I was right. The court was open, well just; I mean the security men at the front door were there. Admin clerks were milling around, but, as there weren't any hearings scheduled for the day, legal personnel were very thin on the ground. They were expecting a district judge during the afternoon, but no one had a clue what time. Terrific! What a brilliant start! Have you ever noticed that nothing goes easily for you when you desperately want it to? At least, not in my experience.

'Let's go and see if we can find the department for me to lodge the cash first, so that we can get one thing organized.'

The security guard was very helpful and explained you have to pledge the bonds first and then you lodge the money. But without a magistrate or a judge nothing could be done.

'Perhaps you should go and have lunch and then in a couple of hours come back and try again.'

'Thank you, but we've driven from London and we would feel better staying in the court area, just in case a judge materialises earlier rather than later.'

We bought cardboard coffees and plastic sandwiches and sat in a waiting area to clock-watch. Uncle Leslie is a quiet, placid man and I was grateful for the non-intrusive, no questions asked quiet time. Laura is a little different, however. She promptly took charge of things, and paced up and down making calls on her mobile and moaning about the situation. I agreed with her completely, but there was nothing we could do about it. I checked my mobile phone and saw a text message from Paul, saying that his surety for ten thousand pounds had been pledged that morning.

'Thank you, Paul and Miri,' I said out loud.

'I wish the judge or whatever he is would hurry up and then we can sort Matt out.'

'Yes, Laura, I agree, but I haven't heard from Carol yet, so even if we can sort it out here, Matt won't be able to come home if there's any kind of hiccup at the court where Carol is!'

I don't know how I managed to say that without becoming emotional. There was Matt waiting hopefully and we had promised him he would definitely be coming home today, and it looked very likely that it wasn't going to happen! Laura mumbled under her breath, Leslie read the notices on the panelled walls and I tried to find out what time a judge was expected, if at all. I was told it could be pot luck as to whether he or she would take an extra day's holiday.

At almost 4 p.m. Mike phoned. 'Claire! Poor Carol has had a wasted time today; there was only a skeleton staff in the court after the Bank Holiday and no one was able to swear her surety, so instead of going to a meeting she has in town tomorrow, she is going back to the court. Hopefully she will see a judge then.'

'Mike! Thank you for phoning. We have a similar problem at the court here, so Matt will have to stay another night and I'll come back to Bristol again tomorrow. Please tell Carol I'm so sorry she has to change her timetable for us, but we are very grateful for her help, and it won't be forgotten.'

'Don't worry, Claire, it can't be helped. Speak to you tomorrow.'

I rang Neil Harvey as I hadn't heard from him since Saturday and explained the situation. 'Mr Harvey, can you possibly phone the prison and give them a message for Matt? He thinks he's coming home tonight and unfortunately it's impossible, as the courts are not fully manned to swear in sureties today. The only one who has been successful is Paul. Matt's Aunt Laura and Uncle Leslie are here in Bristol with me and we are still hoping a judge or magistrate can deal with their bonds and that I can then lodge the cash here, but, even so, Carol can't do hers until tomorrow as the court in Hertfordshire didn't have enough staff today.'

Neil Harvey was amicable; perhaps the long weekend break had put him in a helpful mood. He said he would phone the prison and pass my message on and that he would keep in touch tomorrow with whatever progress Carol achieved and let me know immediately so that Matt could be released. Thanking him I rang off.

At 4.30 a female magistrate arrived. Laura was ushered into the court and I waited outside with Leslie. Ten minutes later Laura came out smiling, as she said it had all gone very smoothly. She'd had to go on the stand and pledge their bonds and had been informed that if Matt tried to leave the country the bonds would automatically belong to the court.

'I hope you answered the magistrate when she said that to you!'

'Yes, of course I did! I said I've known my nephew all his life and he would never do anything like that!'

'Thank you both very much. Now I have to lodge Aunt Bertha's cash.'

I found a security guard who told me that the cashiers were on the first floor. When I had been at the court previously with Geoff I hadn't seen this area. I thought I was at Barclays or NatWest as I joined a short queue of people all putting their monies into a family member who was relying on them for help. How horrible and macabre it all seemed. I eventually arrived at the window and handed over the envelope with Bertha and Marilyn's five thousand pounds, together with the handwritten note to be kept with the monies as a form of security for both Bertie and myself. In return, the cashier handed me a printed receipt from Avon and Somerset Magistrates' Court, Bristol Division. The case number was 1212864, dated 6th May 2003; and it stated 'Cash £5,000, receipt on behalf of Mr M. Davidson.'

'Well, that's a relief. At least we didn't come all this way for nothing.'

I telephoned Helen and Sam and told them how long we had waited to deal with the cash and the bonds but that, thank goodness, it was finally sorted. Sadly, though, we still had to wait for Carol's local court to help her the following day.

'Sorry, Helen, Matt can't come home until sometime tomorrow, so I'll be coming back to Bristol.'

Before I could even ask, Sam, who was on the line listening, said, 'We will go back early tomorrow, Mum. I'm taking you and we'll wait together for Dad. Does he know he can't come home today?'

'I don't know. I have spoken to Neil Harvey and asked him to phone the prison and inform Dad but God knows if they give messages or not. I can't ring him myself, can I? I feel terrible: his hopes were so high and now he'll think we lied to him! I hope he's allowed to ring my mobile or yours later. Then one of us can explain and reassure him.'

'It's not your fault, Mum. It's a load of old bureaucracy.'

'I agree with you, but I can't help feeling bad. Anyway, we're on our way back now so hopefully, depending on rush-hour traffic, we'll see you in about three hours.'

Halfway through our journey my mobile rang. No number or name was displayed but I knew it was Matt. He sounded terrible, like a lost child. 'Claire, is anything happening today? I thought I was going home with you!'

'I'm so sorry, darling. I've been in Bristol for most of the day with Laura and Leslie. The bloody magistrate arrived late this afternoon, and Laura managed to swear her oath at the last minute. I've also lodged the cash, and Paul swore in his surety this morning, so we are almost there. But, unfortunately, Carol's sixty thousand worth of shares cannot be dealt with until tomorrow. She tried so hard to finalize it today, but there wasn't anyone in authority able or available to take it on board. She is very kindly going back to the court somewhere in Hertfordshire tomorrow.'

'Where are you now?' Matt's voice sounded once again very tearful and I wanted to cry.

'On our way back to London. We left Bristol about an hour ago, but Sam and I are coming back tomorrow and as soon as Neil Harvey phones to say it's all been signed, sealed and delivered, we'll be waiting at Horfield for you, no matter what time of day or night it is. Please try to be positive. I know it's easy for me to say this, but it's just one more rung of the ladder we have to climb and you'll be out of there. I wish it could have been today, but the court procedure is absolute rubbish; the right hand doesn't know what the left hand is doing, and we've spent the day hanging around waiting!'

'Okay, Claire, I understand. I feel sorry for you too: you're the one rushing around trying to sort it all out for me and I'm on the waiting side of it all. I have to go now. I'll hopefully see you tomorrow.'

'That was awful. He sounds so upset. I've really let him down.'

'No, you haven't let him down, Claire, the crappy system has,' said Leslie, concentrating on the road but putting his spoke in when needed. 'Let's hope tomorrow we'll get the result we want.'

Helen had once again prepared dinner for all of us and Laura voiced her very definite opinion throughout the meal.

87

'It's absolutely disgraceful. Matt is the last man on earth who should be singled out and subjected to such an ordeal.'

We all agreed with Laura but were powerless to do more than we had at that moment.

9

Wednesday 7th May was a day I will never forget as long as I live. The number seven had always been my Dad's favourite number, so I optimistically hoped the number seven was a good omen. Sam and I once again left London early in the morning and promised Helen faithfully we wouldn't come back without her son.

Arriving at Horfield just after midday I telephoned the solicitor. 'Mr Harvey, we're in Bristol. In fact, we're sitting outside the prison. Can you tell me if you've heard from the court in Hertfordshire where Carol has gone today?'

Neil Harvey was back to his matter-of-fact self and answered simply no, adding that he would get back to me later in the day.

If this story was pure fiction I would probably be able to write about Wednesday 7th May with ease, but as I am writing about an actual series of events I find the facts surrounding that day an emotional roller coaster. Sitting in a car in front of a prison wall waiting for a mobile phone to ring is soul-destroying; it also isn't me! I cannot just wait! I have to do things, try to make things happen. But without any knowledge of court procedure there was nothing to do but wait.

Sam and I agreed that I should phone the prison to see if we could visit Matt. It was now 12.30 p.m. and visiting started at 2, so there wasn't much time to organize it, but if I pleaded our case maybe for once luck would be on our side. I don't know what other prison officers are like, but I have to say that the Horfield telephone operators and their front desk personnel are extremely amicable. Another friendly voice came to our rescue, 'No problem, Mrs Davidson, your husband wouldn't be released until after visiting time anyway, so you can see him this afternoon.'

'Okay, Sam, that's sorted! We have to go now to a side office near the main entrance to collect two passes. Whoever I just spoke to was as helpful as the man on Saturday. He said that if Dad was going to be allowed to leave the prison today it wouldn't be until after the visit was over, and that he was sure it would break the monotony.'

I telephoned Mr Harvey and left him a voice message on his mobile to tell him Sam and I were seeing Matt and would have our mobiles switched off until 3 p.m. so if he had any news before then could he please leave me a message. I also spoke to Carol, who sounded absolutely fraught with frustration. The time she had spent at the court was ridiculous and she didn't appear to be getting anywhere very fast. I realized we were indebted to her kindness, and was worried that she would get aggravated with the situation and walk out of the court, which would mean that Matt wouldn't be able to walk anywhere outside of the prison walls. I wasn't thinking clearly; Carol would never walk out! She was pragmatic and also sympathetic to Matt's cause and I knew she wouldn't let us down. But I couldn't vouch for the system in which the courts worked not letting us all down. Sam was talking to a friend on her mobile and I didn't want to tell Matt and Sam for the moment that Carol was having problems again. I decided to play it by ear.

We walked past the main doors, found a small office and gave the man our names. He ticked us off in a book and handed us two passes. The queue was considerably shorter than it had been on Monday. We went through the same scenario as we did before with the same smiling desk officer or whatever his title is. He was a nice 'meet and greet' man who I thought made Horfield more approachable. We took our key to a locker and went to the X-ray machine. This time we didn't need to ask anyone for help as sadly we knew what to do, let's hope for the very last time! A gloved individual who didn't make you feel the place was approachable one little bit checked our hair thoroughly, but, thank goodness, allowed us to go through after that. I really thought she was going to check my teeth and tell me I needed a filling. We tentatively walked past the ever-so-friendly playful pet of the year, who looked even more hungry for blood than he had on Monday, and into the cafeteria.

By now more visitors had arrived and the place was filling up. There were fewer families and children, and more individuals this time. We bought chocolate bars and tea and when Matt saw us he looked very surprised.

'I only found out a while ago that I had a visitor and assumed it was the solicitor Neil Harvey. I'm happy to see you two instead though. So what's happening?'

'Sam drove us here. We left London as usual at 9 a.m. and we've been here since midday. We are waiting for Carol to complete her surety, so we thought it made sense to see you, even though you're coming back with us later.'

'How are you feeling, Dad?'

'I'm all right, a bit jaded I think the word is. It's just the same old same old, plus waiting around staring at the four walls. Have you spoken to Carol since you've been here?'

I lied. 'Yes! But only very briefly as we have to hand our mobiles in here, so there could be a very good chance that both Carol and Mr Harvey have left messages.'

'Dad, whatever time you are allowed to leave we will be waiting for you.'

I could see Matt was on the verge of tears so told him snippets of useless small talk, even discussing football tactics at West Ham, anything to lighten the conversation. After a group hug and a promise we would be back for him in an hour or two, said with my fingers crossed behind my back, we watched him go back with the other inmates. As I write this I feel sad remembering how he looked walking next to the other men from his wing, or block, or whatever it's called.

Collecting our mobiles we switched them on but I didn't have one single message.

'Mum, it's not good enough! We only have two hours before deadline!'

'I know. Let's go and ask the desk officer if he knows the procedure.'

I explained that we were waiting to take Mr Davidson home and was there anyone I could ask who could tell us if things were moving in the right direction. He told us to go into the administrative office where they deal with all the paperwork, as they'd be able to tell us if they'd had any communication from the court.

'Sorry, Mrs Davidson, we don't know. We have been informed that your husband was due to be released today, but as of now we are still waiting for notification that this can actually happen. And until we receive written confirmation our hands are tied.'

'What do you suggest we do?'

'Keep trying your husband's solicitor, who should be keeping you up to date.'

Dejected, I smiled weakly. 'Thank you for your help anyway; it's appreciated.'

'Mum, this is awful! Nobody knows what's going on! Or maybe they do, but aren't saying!'

I rang Mike, but he hadn't heard from Carol for quite a while, so didn't know if she was still waiting in the court or not. He could probably tell from my voice that I was at my wits' end but there wasn't anything he could do. Neil Harvey was next, and I was surprised he took my call. He'd sounded fed up with me ringing before, but as far as I was concerned too bad! Matt's freedom was at stake and I couldn't have cared less what the solicitor thought. I think that's the good part of growing old: you can get away with so much more, say what you think and to hell with the consequences!

'Mrs Davidson, you do realize we only have until 5 p.m. to inform the prison and make it all happen for Matt?'

'Yes, I'm fully aware of that! Why do you think I keep on ringing you?'

'I realize you're worried, but there's nothing we can do. It's out of our hands until we get the nod from the court where Carol is. I'll keep trying them and I'll then let you know.'

'Thank you, Mr Harvey.'

We sat in the car for ages just staring blankly at the bloody wall. Sam said it was an impossible, dire, frustrating situation that we would normally just read about, and I said I'd stupidly thought that England was a democratic country. That's crap for a start; there's so many hidden grey areas below the surface that Joe public haven't got a clue about. I felt sorry for Helen too, as she was waiting for news and I didn't want to phone her at that moment. I didn't know what to say to her!

'Mum! Sitting outside this wall watching prison officers patrol the area with their guard dogs is driving me mad! I'm sorry, I can't stand it anymore; I need a cigarette! I did give up smoking but right now it's on a back burner.'

'I understand. If I had smoked in the past I would have gone through a couple of packets today. Instead I am wearing my gums away chewing like a football manager and probably giving myself stomach ulcers and goodness knows what else!'

'I haven't any cigarettes with me, so let's get away from this grotty scenery and find a corner shop or supermarket.' Sam drove about a mile down the road where there was a small parade of shops. Her skin was a shade of deathly white, and I was really worried about her. I watched her crossing the road; her shoulders were slouched and her body language shouted 'defeated'! How did we know if the solicitor was ringing the court or not, pushing for the judge to see Carol? I doubted it very much. There was never a trace of compassion in his voice and most of the time he gave me the impression that he believed my husband was a 'master criminal'. Rather an ignorant observation actually, because if he had been on the wrong side of the law, our reaction towards the raid and our total behaviour would have been very different. We would have dealt with it all in a more matter-of-fact way. Matt is so squeaky clean that my anger was rising to boiling point.

Sam returned with a bar of chocolate to keep me going and she walked up and down the street nervously smoking as though her life depended on it, just trying to keep calm. It didn't look as though it was working. I felt sure that at any moment she would become unhinged and explode. Staring out of the car window watching Sam, I glanced at my lifeless mobile phone, willing it to ring, but was met with silence. By now in the cinema heavy music would be being played to emphasize the situation in all its dramatic form. All I knew was that each day my husband stayed banged up for something he hadn't done, he'd go a little more downhill. I wasn't sure if he would be able to survive.

Sam came back to the car at 4.50 and once again I rang Neil Harvey to be told by whoever answered the phone that he was on an urgent call but that if there was any news he would contact me.

'You know, Sam, I have clock-watched since last Wednesday. I've wasted precious hours simply checking the time. This is all pointless and I'm going crazy. Any suggestions?'

'Yes! We are not going back to London tonight without Dad. The way things are going he probably won't leave until tomorrow, so if we have to we'll buy toothbrushes and find a bed and breakfast near here. If there isn't one we'll just have to slum it and stay in the car all night staring at the prison.

Whatever it takes to bring Dad home we have to do it, and until he's free we wait!'

'Yes, I agree. We'll do whatever we have to and drive around and look for a guest house near the bloody prison. But, unfortunately as time is ticking away, Dad doesn't know what's going on, and I can't imagine what Carol is going through. She must be very upset she's lost two days simply hanging around. I don't trust the court, the police, none of them! It's all very peculiar and I may be a cynic, but doesn't it seem contrived that nobody has been able to deal with Carol's surety on either day? It's all a plot instigated by the dreaded Clarke: he and the powers that be have decided to make Dangerous Davidson sit it out for as long as possible, and, no matter how hard I try, none of it makes one tiny bit of sense.'

The clock was against us. We had five minutes left before the dreaded deadline.

'Nothing's going to happen now; it's almost 5 p.m.' As I said those words, my phone rang. Neil Harvey's number registered.

'Mrs Davidson, it's sorted! Matt can be released shortly. Carol has finally been able to pledge her oath, which has now gone through, and I've spoken to Horfield and given them your number. They will be phoning you to let you know the procedure and you can then collect your husband.'

I may not have bonded with Mr Harvey but at that moment he was the most wonderful human being on earth. 'That's fantastic news and a huge relief. Thank you very much for letting me know.'

'There will be a hearing at the court again, I'm afraid. It's in Bristol on Friday morning. But you enjoy your evening and I'll speak to Matt tomorrow.'

Sam and I hugged and started singing 'He's coming home, he's coming home …'.

'Let's drive back to the prison so that we can be there

waiting for him. Oh Mum, thank goodness!' Sam smiled for the first time in a week. The wall may have stuck out like a sore thumb but we no longer cared. We would never see the place again after today so another few minutes wouldn't matter.

Without visitors we were able to park by the side of the entrance, and as it was now getting chilly we stayed in the car. A few minutes later a prison officer called and the conversation went something like this.

'Mrs Davidson, your husband is free to leave here. We just have to finalize the papers, but it shouldn't take too long.'

'Thank you. We have parked near the entrance, so we'll come and wait outside for him. Is that all right?'

'Yes, of course. Good luck, Mrs Davidson.'

'Thank you. Goodbye.'

'Come on, Mum, let's go and wait outside. I don't want to keep looking at the wall. I'd rather be right where the main door is when Dad comes out.'

'I'll phone Helen whilst we're waiting, and Carol.'

Helen sounded so relieved. 'What time will you be back'?

'I honestly don't know, but as soon as he comes out he'll phone you. Go and make yourself a cup of tea and relax. At least this time we have good news and hopefully it can only get better ...'

'Thank you for letting me know, Claire. I'll put supper on as soon as I hear from Matt.'

'Your grandmother spends her life thinking of what to make foodwise. She should have owned a restaurant.'

I phoned Carol and Mike and told them Matt would be out soon, thanks to Carol's efforts. I said Matt would be phoning to thank her himself!

'I can't imagine how much paperwork there is to do! We've been standing out here for almost half an hour and I'm checking the time again! I don't know about you, Sam, but I'm feeling cold.'

'Okay, Mum. Here's where my dance teaching moves come into play.' Our light-hearted daughter was back, thank goodness, and I didn't mind one little bit when she grabbed hold of me and jigged me around in a lively off-the-cuff dance routine in front of the main entrance. I doubt if I would have won any medals for technique as I am certainly not known as a dancing queen but I didn't care.

I looked at the side of the door and noticed a mirror and heard laughter from behind it. Then the friendly desk officer came out and said, 'We can see you through the two-way mirror dancing up and down, obviously much happier now!'

'We'll be happier still when he comes out! How long does it take?'

'Shouldn't be too long. He has to see the governor and that's it!'

Sam and I were like two children, jumping around because we were so happy. But an hour passed and I began to wonder if we were the main characters in a sick joke! Where was Matt? How long does it take to say "Goodbye" and "Sign your name here"? Standing outside the main door, which was on a par with the great wall, I listened intently to try and hear any sound, but of course it was impossible. No sound could penetrate through the thickness of the door.

A moment later the door was pushed open and at long last Matt was free. We huddled together in front of the mirror and I'm not sure if I imagined it but I thought I heard a faint cheer from the other side.

'Oh Dad, we're so happy. We can't begin to explain what happened; we were on a knife's edge. It appears Carol was only seen just before the five p.m. deadline. Mum and I were so worried you would have to spend another night here that we were going to look for a place to stay, just so that we didn't have to go back to London and return early tomorrow. Plus we wanted to be near to you.'

'Thank you both for everything. Come on, let's not hang around here any longer. I'm so glad to be out of here.'

We all linked arms and held on to Matt tightly, afraid to let him go.

'Matt, we brought your post; it's all on the back seat. Do you want to sit there or drive?'

'No, Claire, I'm happy in the back. I'll read the bills and phone my mum. When we get back I'll speak to Paul, Carol and Mike, and in the morning I'll phone Geoff and Laura.'

This time driving back to London was a happy event, and glancing at Matt reading his Inland Revenue letters and general correspondence it was hard to tell whether the terrible experience had scarred him emotionally. I wondered how he would cope with whatever Clarke had in store for him, because I felt sure it wasn't over by a long way. From the little I knew about the police it wasn't difficult to see that Matt was being used. Anyway no good worrying about what might be! For now he was free! May it last forever! We spent the journey talking about light-hearted matters, although I did have to tell him that Neil Harvey had mentioned another short hearing in Bristol on Friday morning, so it looked like we'd be back on the M4 again very soon.

'Okay, we'll go back tomorrow and perhaps book the same hotel where you all stayed last Friday.'

'Yes, all right darling. I'll organize it in the morning. At least this time we won't be staying at the court all day like last Friday. Apparently this is just a very quick routine hearing so nothing to worry about for a change!'

Helen was waiting outside the house when we approached the drive. It reminded me of the time when Matt's football team had won the FA Cup, a long time ago, and Helen had put handmade banners and scarves outside the windows. I wouldn't have put it past her, in between cooking a three-course dinner, to have found some spare material and in two minutes on her sewing machine sewn a

'Matt's Free!' flag and draped it along the front path. Perhaps not! Anyway, after Helen had given Matt one of her arm's length Helen style hugs and he in turn, in very similar fashion, had patted her on the back, we walked into her house with mixed feelings. Relief was on the top of the list, but creeping up to topple it was fear. At least I felt that!

Helen's house didn't have a friendly ambience for me at all. It just made me think of early morning raids and police in every room. I knew that if it had been a rented house we wouldn't have stayed, but as it was Helen's home it was a very different matter. Helen had invited Laura and Leslie to dinner and they made the right noises and said positive things. Matt phoned Carol and Mike before dinner to thank them and, after we had eaten one of Helen's excellent meals, he phoned Geoff. When he told him we were going back to Bristol the next day Geoff said he would join us. Laura and Leslie also said they would come, so it was left for me to find a hotel with three rooms available. Forgive me if that sounds like I was ungrateful, but it was beginning to sound like a jolly day out and I still had my doubts! Laura said they would be over late afternoon and we would all go to eat somewhere locally, preferably Italian, before heading for Bristol after the rush hour.

Sam and Helen went to bed about 11 p.m. and Sam was beginning to look like our daughter again. Hopefully she would start to enjoy her life. She had been a wonderful rock and support to Helen and me and words cannot express how thankful we felt to have her as our daughter and grand-daughter.

10

'Matt, now we're alone, tell me how you really feel? We haven't really talked about your terrible ordeal and I know I've only written children's books, but I want to write your story. Do you think one day you'll be able to talk about it and tell me what happened when those bloody bastards took you to Bristol'?

'Claire! I'm quite okay to talk about it now.'

'Are you sure? I don't want to make you feel any pressure. You've been through enough of that the past week!'

'No, it will be good to get it off my chest.'

'All right. Let me get my notebook and pen. I don't think I'm going to hear a funny *Frasier* story, so I'm going to continue with my nightly habit and pour myself a brandy. You don't want one, do you?'

'Ugh, no! A cup of good coffee would be nice though!'

Sipping brandy and coffee together in companionable silence felt very comforting whilst I waited in some trepidation for Matt to unwind and begin to talk.

'When I left the house with the three arresting officers, don't ask me why, but I didn't realize how serious it was and the implications. I kept thinking "This won't take long; they'll probably ask me a few questions, write some details and I'll be home in time to take Samantha to Bournemouth." They took me to the local police station in Colindale where I had to hand in my mobile and any money I had on me. In fact everything and anything was taken and put in a see-through plastic bag. Then I was told, "Come with us, Sir," and I was

100

whisked off immediately by the same officers. I sat in between two of the policemen in the back of a dark navy or black saloon car. We chatted quite amiably about football and, halfway through the journey along the motorway, I asked where we were going. "We are going to Bristol, Sir." The first thing that entered my head, Claire, wasn't "Why am I going to Bristol?" I stupidly said, "I'm going to Bournemouth with my daughter this afternoon; will I be back in time?" One of the officers blandly replied, "We don't know, Sir." Further along the M4 we stopped at a service station and a police officer bought me a newspaper and coffee. When we finally arrived at the police station I saw it was in the middle of nowhere, but, instead of asking questions like you probably would, I still thought it was something based on a routine enquiry, until I was escorted into the station and put immediately in a cell. I am being polite when I say it was something out of Dickens. It consisted of a bench seat, a paper thin blue mattress – no blankets, no duvet, no covers at all – a broken toilet that only flushed from the outside of the cell, and no wash basin. The floor was concrete, which made it freezing, and there was a slat in the door where they fed slop to me. Food not fit to be given to an animal. I lived off coffee.

'It was explained to me that the police needed to ask me questions, but were unable to commence doing so until I had a solicitor present. They suggested I should have a local solicitor from Bristol to expedite matters. I declined the offer as I was allowed one call to you, and I was thankful that you had managed to contact Paul early in the morning, and that he had kindly arranged for a London solicitor to come to Bristol and help me. The downside of it was that I had to stay in the cell until Mr Harvey arrived. He came at about 2 p.m. and they put me in an interview room. Two policemen called Kershaw and Porter put a tape in a machine that was so distorted it was hard to understand who was allegedly speaking. I was told by Policeman Porter that it was Adrienne

Carter, Jennifer Thornton and Me. To my ears it sounded more like three chipmunks. There was a good deal of background noise and I couldn't tell who was saying what. As I had never heard my voice on audio tape before it didn't sound like me at all. The interview session was set to end at around 4 p.m. and they said they had another tape to play to me, but needed to interview Jennifer that evening and resume our interview the following day. So, I was left in the cell for the rest of the afternoon and evening, where I was absolutely frozen. I wasn't offered any blankets and the heating had been turned off. I used my coat as a pillow and alternated it as a blanket. I couldn't sleep. I couldn't for the life of me understand why I was being treated like a number one criminal. I realized this was once again to do with the Carter family, but after Clarke had told us both to get on with our lives and that everything was in order back in 2001, what on earth was this all about?

'The following day, Thursday 1st May, I was given a sensational breakfast of microwaved burnt sausage and sliced potatoes. It was as awful as the previous day's so-called lunch and dinner, so once again I didn't eat anything. At about midday, Neil Harvey telephoned the police station and the duty officer allowed me to speak to him. He asked how I was and I told him "Not very good." He explained that the police weren't coming to interview me yet as they were still interviewing Jennifer Thornton. He asked if I wanted him to buy me any food as he would be coming in later. He bought me sandwiches and cakes from M & S and pushed them through the slat. To me it was the most wonderful food imaginable! Late in the afternoon I was once again taken into an interview room and Kershaw and Porter played another tape to me, just as crackly as the tape before. Then they bombarded me with questions. All my answers were "No comment" on the advice of my solicitor. Then the interview was finished. Kershaw, I think it was, listed four charges that he read out on the computer and then he asked me to sign, which I refused to do as it contained numerous lies. My solicitor Mr Harvey said it wouldn't matter whether I signed it or not, but I definitely didn't want to.

'Soon afterwards Kershaw and Porter were joined by a policeman known as a bail officer. I was led to believe that he would have an impartial view of whether Kershaw and Porter were right in refusing me bail. Of course, it was a fait accompli, as can you imagine a policeman going against his colleagues, no matter what they said or did? Neil Harvey asked Porter if I could be released on bail and he said he would have to check with his boss. I knew it had to be Clarke; I can't believe for one minute it was anyone else. Kershaw and Porter returned after a lengthy conversation and told Neil and me they would object to bail based on the fact that I might abscond or interfere with potential witnesses! By then it was all going completely over my head. The bail officer told Neil that as you were coming down later that evening you could see me if you arrived before 10 p.m.'

'I was never told that! I'm so sorry, I had no idea! I would have demanded to see you if someone had had the decency to tell me. God, what a load of bastards they are! I feel so sad listening to you and how you were treated. It's totally mind-blowing. Do you want to carry on telling me, or are you tired?'

'No, I'm in full flow. Anyway at about 9 p.m. a duty officer came into my cell and asked me if everything was all right. Was I warm enough? Had I eaten? I answered no, of course I wasn't, pointing out the mattress without any covers for starters. He said he would try and sort it out, but I'm still waiting for that miracle as I never saw him again and nothing changed. I put the blame in Clarke's corner. He probably thought that if I suffered enough I would tell all I knew. The problem was that I knew nothing! I kept awake, which wasn't very difficult under the circumstances, with my eyes on stalks waiting for you to arrive, and I'm sure I heard your voice saying thank you to the duty officer and goodbye. I felt very sad, as I knew you had gone and weren't able to see me. Without the comfort of even saying hello to you, I sat on the hard bench all night in a kind of daze and froze as I had done the night before.

'I hadn't been given the opportunity until Friday morning to brush my teeth or wash my hands, and I felt awful. But, because I was due to go to the magistrates' court and you had brought in an overnight bag with clothes, a wash bag and a lovely handwritten note that bucked me up a bit, I was allowed at 8 a.m. the privilege of a cordoned off section outside my cell, which led to a shower and sink where I was able to shave and wash properly. I had plenty of time for this, as I'd been told that Reliance security were coming for me at 8.30 so I didn't have to rush. I then dressed and was immediately handcuffed and escorted from my cell to the security van for the short journey to Bristol magistrates' court. I was taken to a back entrance of the court where the cells were and again put into a cell, but this time with another man who was asleep on a bench. I initially stood up and after about fifteen or twenty minutes used my coat as a cushion. I sat on the floor for ages.

'At about 10 a.m. I was taken by a guard and handcuffed again, waiting outside the court room with the security guard. There were five other co-defendants already waiting there and I recognised three of them to be Matthew and Adrienne Carter and Jennifer Thornton. They looked shocked when they saw me, but to be frank, Claire, I wasn't with it at all by then. It was as if the stuffing had been taken out of me and I barely acknowledged them. We were all led into the court and put behind a long glass dock, as you saw for yourself. The security guards sat directly behind each defendant. I had never seen the other two male defendants who were with us and I felt as though I was in a terrible dream, which if I blinked hard enough I would wake from! I noticed you and Geoff immediately, plus Neil Harvey sitting in the middle of the court and my arch enemy Martin Clarke, who looked like the cat who had eaten all the cream. I can't say how I felt really. I knew you were there, as I just said, but I felt as though my own spirit had gone somewhere else. It's hard to explain.

'I know you heard the same words as I did in court and saw the same people, so I won't go over it all in detail. But there were differences in the angle you saw it all from, as I know you will understand and appreciate. I'll tell you the bits that happened separately to me in my dazed state. When the session was adjourned for lunch we were put back into our original cells and offered food and drink through the hole in the top of the cell door. I was taken back up again at 2.20 p.m. which was when each defendant's solicitor said his piece. A great deal of the time my mind was drifting and I couldn't concentrate. I remember the various solicitors talking about sureties and how much monies were on offer from their respective clients for the magistrate to consider.

'After Clarke went on the stand, my solicitor introduced Paul's letter as part of his appraisal of me. Before it was handed to the magistrate he read it out loud for us all to hear. I think you missed that bit, Claire, as I remember you leaving the court for a moment. Maybe you went to the toilet? Anyway, Paul wrote a brilliant letter that I really appreciated, saying it was absolutely preposterous and that if he hadn't been at a hearing in a London court himself that afternoon he would have made the long journey to Bristol to support me. By the way, I don't know if you noticed, but when Harvey was asking Clarke whether anything incriminating had been found in our house I thought it very strange that two of the arresting officers who schlepped me to Bristol and questioned me at the police station were nowhere to be seen in the court room. That meant they couldn't be questioned!'

'Matt, I noticed this and I even told Geoff. It's all very fishy and smells to high heaven!'

'When you went on the stand and condemned the whole scenario, I heard every word you said, especially the West Ham and wine gums part. And thank you for bringing my passport to the court; you have very good foresight. I actually gave myself false hope that I would be going home with you that evening. However, it wasn't going to happen was it? Although the magistrate had finally granted me bail at about 5.15 p.m. there wasn't any time to arrange the surety until the following Tuesday, which meant I had to languish in a Bristol prison. Without any criminal record, I didn't know what to expect or what I was going into. I felt very alone. The entire situation was unreal. I was escorted downstairs and asked for my National Insurance number by a court security officer. I was then told I would be taken to prison shortly. Neil Harvey spoke very briefly to me and again I was handcuffed and taken to a prison van which had compartments so you couldn't see other prisoners.

'Sitting in the van I looked out the window at the cars and buses passing by. I cannot describe how I felt. I just kept thinking "This cannot be happening to me!" The drive was about fifteen minutes, although it seemed a lifetime. When we arrived at the prison reception area, our names were called out one by one, and I was the last one out. Again, any possessions I had, that you had put in my overnight bag, had to be handed over and then they checked my details. We all sat in a room and waited again for our names to be called, when we had to strip off and be frisked, losing our one little remaining bit of dignity completely. I was given a choice: I could wear my own clothes or the wonderful Armani prison gear. I chose my own. I then had my photo taken, like the common criminal I am, with a number against it and my fingerprints. They told me they had run out of stocks of toiletries, so there was no toothpaste, deodorant or shampoo, and only one blanket per person. I was getting used to the high life! I was then led round to the C wing and allocated a cell. I was asked if I would like to share. The reception officer was actually a decent man, approachable, and he said he would put me with someone who was a "good bloke", whatever that means! It was about 8 p.m. by then and prison supper had been over hours ago. But latecomers get offered a choice of curry or pasta, so obviously I chose pasta.

'Carrying my blanket and pillow into the cafeteria I was given a mountain of pasta, a lemon sponge pudding, a roll and butter and a cup of tea. It reminded me of the conveyor belt on *The Generation Game*, only this wasn't part of a TV game show and I couldn't get out. I ate half the meal and was then taken to meet my room mate, a man in his thirties who looked quite a bit older. Pete was a petty thief and a very friendly character. He offered to show me the ropes, which I was grateful for. As there weren't any fresh supplies I had been allowed to keep my own toothbrush and Pete lent me his toothpaste. I was given the top bunk and went to bed about 10 p.m. The next morning I was given a couple of towels and told showers started at 8 a.m. There were six showers near our cell, all in one long line, and once I had showered and dressed, Pete told me to go down to the cafeteria to get my breakfast, which on a weekend was a full English. It wasn't like a hotel version, though, by any stretch of the imagination. The egg was powdered, the beans were soggy, and the bacon was streaky. We all took our food on a tray back to our en-suite accommodation, and queued for boiling water from an urn near the cells to make our own tea or coffee. It was by then only 9 a.m. Saturday morning. Normally at that time, as you know, I'm watching Sky Sports and taking a long, leisurely bath. Unless there's a home game and then I'm off to watch The Hammers. So it all seemed really weird – abnormal, unfamiliar and completely alien to anything I could possibly get used to. I lay on my bunk and watched TV although I didn't know what I was watching.

'At 10.30 the prison officers came round to the cells and unlocked them and we were allowed to have some exercise in the prison yard. That basically entailed strolling around a large playground for about an hour. I had a chat with a few people but began to feel a little uncomfortable. I asked one of the wardens if I could use the loo. He made a request through an intercom, but nobody came, and my need got progressively worse, despite other inmates asking on my behalf, including Matt Carter, who could see I was in pain. I was eventually allowed back to my cell five minutes before everyone else. Whether it was delayed shock, I don't know, but I had a bout of sickness and diarrhoea and felt terrible. Prison lunchtime was early, 11.30 a.m. That's late morning to me! Queuing for lunch was a momentous occasion. Each prisoner gave their name with their order. As I hadn't been in the situation before I didn't know about any order! One of the kitchen staff called out to me, "Fishburger!" Everyone was called by their surname, and I assumed he thought my surname was "Fishburger". I answered "No! Davidson!" He looked at me as though I was a moron and again he said "Fishburger!" I told him, "That isn't my name. It's Davidson!" But he told me, "No mate, you're having a fishburger and mash and a school dinner dessert, jam roly poly." I actually thought my mistake was quite funny and laughed to myself.'

'Matt, thank goodness you haven't lost your sense of humour! It's very funny and I have to admit that after listening intently to such serious stuff, this little comic episode is very welcome. Plus, I shouldn't think there are any inmates with a name like Fishburger in Bristol!'

'Anyway, I ate lunch in my cell with Pete, and then watched television again. At 3 p.m. we were allowed association, which means that the whole of the C Wing could go into the games room, which consisted of a snooker table,

table tennis and a bigger TV. I was given fifty pence credit and a computerised PIN, which meant I could make a phone call. I went to the warden and asked to make one call to you and he put me on a list. Then after a while he called me. I phoned you and cried when I heard your voice. You actually lightened the conversation by telling me that everyone cries when they speak to you! I was happy when you said you were coming with Sam and Mum on Monday to see me and hopeful when you said I should be released on Tuesday, but after my call I felt very depressed and alone and I went back to the cell to wait for the very early supper, at 5.30. I was beginning to learn the pattern: eat, watch television and sleep. We were locked in for the rest of the night. The only thing I was looking forward to was *Match of the Day*, and getting a glimpse of one of my favourite footballers, Paulo di Canio, scoring a goal for The Hammers against Chelsea.

'On Sunday the same routine applied, except after breakfast there was Kit Day, which meant that, if you were a long-term prisoner, you were given freshly laundered tracksuits, thick socks and boxer shorts, plus fresh bedding and an extra blanket. I was on remand for the short term, but I didn't have a change of clothes, so they gave me a grey and maroon tracksuit. I would then be able to give my clothes into the laundry room as I had been wearing them for a while. I was given razors, a shaving brush, a shaving stick, a toothbrush and paste, deodorant and some shampoo sachets. By lunchtime I was asked if I would like to change my cell, as Pete's friend was next door to us and he was sharing with Brian Dorfmann, one of the Carter defendants I had never met before. I took my bedding, my new toiletries and my own plastic plate, mug and cutlery to the en-suite next to Pete's. By the afternoon I was sharing my cell with Brian, who had the whitest teeth I've ever seen. He must have spent a fortune on new porcelain choppers, or whatever they do with professional whitening, but somehow they didn't blend in with the surroundings. He was a pleasant enough man and we passed the time having small talk. Once again the rest of the day was spent watching television and eating and trying not to think too much, which is easier said than done when you have so much time on your hands.

'On Bank Holiday Monday, I was aware I was having a visit from all of you, and I tried to look my best, which was very difficult under the circumstances. I was collected at 1.40 for a forty-five minute visit, beginning at 2 p.m. We had to prepare for this by walking across from our wing and picking up other inmates along the way who were also having visitors. When we arrived at the main building we had to book into a reception area where a warden took details of names of visitors. We were then issued with a state-of-the-art orange bib and were called one by one into the large cafeteria area where you were all waiting patiently. I found it very hard to see the three of you for such a short time. It was so soon over. But I was boosted by the overwhelming support and promises that once the surety had been sanctioned I would be free. I returned to my cell and watched the end of a film – *It's A Mad, Mad, Mad, Mad World* – which felt very apt in my case.

'Tuesday gave me more hope that something positive was going to happen! Early in the afternoon we were requested to gather for an integration meeting, which introduced you to the running of the prison. This was all done on video and lasted for an hour with interjections from the officer in charge. We were given tea and told we could ask questions. At the end of the hour we were taken back to our cell and then it was time for association again. We were issued our shopping requests and I was able to buy mineral water, fabric conditioner, strong mints and some more telephone credit. I wanted to phone you as I was unsure what was happening to me, and didn't know what was happening with the surety! When I rang you on your mobile and you told me you had been in Bristol all day with Leslie and Laura but were on your way home, I must have sounded very tearful, but you reassured me that it was only Carol's surety that needed to be finalized. When you told me that would be done on Wednesday and that you and Sam were coming back to Bristol first thing the following day to wait for me, I rang off feeling optimistic.

'After breakfast on Wednesday I saw on a notice board the heading "Runners", whatever that meant, with my name under it. Pete explained that I was going to have a visit in the afternoon, although no one had so far told me. I assumed it would be Neil Harvey but was very pleasantly surprised to see you and Samantha instead. Again I felt very hopeful as you had both been in Bristol for most of the day and you said you wouldn't leave without me. I went back to the cell and told Brian I hoped to be released very shortly, and then I waited and waited and waited, becoming more and more despondent. At 5 p.m. a warden came to the cell and told me to get my things. I knew I was being released, but I wasn't prepared for the leaving party. I was taken to see the prison governor who said that all my papers were in order. I was given my clothes in a carrier bag and told I had to go into a holding room, allegedly for a few minutes. It was a very narrow cupboard-sized room with a small bench, a door and no outside window. You know how much I hate lifts without windows and I began to feel claustrophobic, but I knew it was my final hurdle. However, a few minutes in prison terms really meant the best part of an hour! I listened to people walking past the door and I became very frustrated and tried to attract attention by banging on it. Eventually a prison officer came and told me they were working on my papers and wouldn't be long now. I must have sounded like a child, as I told him I thought they'd forgotten I was in there. He said of course they hadn't. After an age I was allowed out of the cupboard where the governor handed me copy papers of sureties and I had to sign a paper stating that I had received my belongings and that everything had been given back to me, except of course my mobile, which Clarke has probably taken apart by now and lost all my very criminal West Ham texts! The prison governor told me he hoped he didn't see me again and I assured him he wouldn't. I walked out of the reception area into a poor man's courtyard and was escorted to the main door. Then I was free! So there you have it in all its Technicolor glory. My wonderful, happy week at the funny farm! I'm going to sleep now, Claire. I feel very tired and it will make a nice change to spend the night in a comfortable bed!'

'Yes, try and have a good night. I feel really humbled by what you've said and I'm going to stay down here for a while longer. Sleep is something I haven't been used to since last Wednesday, so it's going to take me some time to get into the sleep mode again. I can't find the right words to tell you how happy we are to have you home!'

'You don't have to say anything, I know you all care. Thanks for everything, Claire. Goodnight.'

I poured another brandy and thought that if the case carried on for much longer I would need Alcoholics Anonymous! Every word, every line Matt had dictated to me, made my blood boil!

What a terrible, horrible experience, poor man! There we were here, all feeling down in the dumps thinking we were going through a bad week. But we could all come and go as we pleased. We may have come up against inconvenience, a great deal of travelling, lack of sleep and the obvious worrying, but it was nothing in comparison to the inhuman treatment Matt had received, and for what? Being in the wrong place at the wrong time! Or worse still, guilty by association! How could Clarke and his team of misfits call themselves 'the law'? It was all a fictitious load of old twaddle! A false, fitted-up version of fairy stories that only benefitted a ghastly man like Clarke! How vile! The way Matt had been treated you would have thought he was guilty of the most heinous, odious crimes!

When I finally went to bed it was with great relief at seeing Matt sleeping peacefully. I watched him in wonder. If it had been me in his position I wouldn't have taken it all so calmly. But, although Matt was home, I still couldn't get to sleep. There was far too much going on in my brain, such as what was going to happen in the bloody court in Bristol on Friday!

11

We all ate breakfast together the next morning as though nothing different had transpired in our lives.

'Neil Harvey is on the ball this morning, Claire. He rang me when you were in the shower. Apparently the hearing tomorrow should only last ten minutes. He didn't feel it necessary to go all the way to Bristol and charge us for his time as it's just a routine kind of roll call of names, nothing very dramatic, so he's instructed a local solicitor, Lawrence Travers, who works near the court. However, it's possible that a London barrister, Alex Landers, will introduce himself too. Neil says he's very good and Paul knows him as well. So tomorrow we have nothing to worry about. It shouldn't be too difficult; we'll probably be home just after lunch!'

I wasn't so optimistic, but I didn't say anything to Matt. I hoped I was wrong!

After spending the morning sorting out a Bristol hotel with three available rooms, I phoned a few of Matt's colleagues who had all kindly enquired about his health. I told them all he should be back on his feet by Monday and would contact them himself after the weekend. Matt went with Sam and bought another mobile phone. Neither of us is very technical and our daughter's expertise was needed.

I am now probably going to sound very mean-spirited to anyone reading this who doesn't know me, but driving to Bristol listening to Geoff drone on an on and on as though he was Judge Judy, Perry Mason and Judge John Deed all rolled into one was driving me mad! Luckily for Laura and Leslie they appeared to have turned off. I tried to follow suit, but I kept thinking what if tomorrow doesn't go well? What if Neil Harvey should be in court with Matt? What if we come up against a problem? What if...? Two little words with a huge meaning. I was making myself increasingly depressed. I had to cheer up, or I would be no help to my husband who had been calmly listening to Geoff's words of wisdom for almost three hours. Thankfully none of us wanted to make a night of it so we all retreated to our rooms ready for an early start the next day.

The following morning we all arrived at the court. After checking into security we looked around for Lawrence Travers. A man with a kind face came over and introduced himself. 'We need to find a conference room so I can have as many facts from you, Mr Davidson, as possible.'

I watched Geoff as he took charge and found the room, and I admit I found his actions a little peculiar. How much does he even like Matt? Or how much is this just an exciting adventure for him? I told myself off again for having such negative thoughts about a good friend.

Mr Travers was a middle-aged man with a soft voice and a very pleasant manner. After Matt had finished condensing the scenario, he told us not to worry and that it wouldn't be too long in court. Then Alex Landers arrived.

Mr Landers seemed friendly enough. He didn't know Lawrence Travers but they discussed the case in more legal terms than we could. Geoff made a few faces, as Alex Landers had taken over and it was no longer Geoff's show. I listened with Laura and Leslie to hypothetical comments and questions that Matt answered accordingly. Although Alex Landers was obviously extremely capable and by all accounts a very competent barrister, his parting remark before he went to change into the wonderful wig and gown was not something we would have expected from someone of his calibre. Looking directly at Matt he rubbed his hands together in a gleeful way and said, 'This is Premier League!' I know my husband loves to talk about football, but nothing had been mentioned so far about football matches, so Alex Landers was referring to the Carters as the legal fraternity within the circle of the criminal court club, knowing that this case was going to be a big one.

I didn't know if anyone else had picked up on it but I wanted a barrister to look at Matt and, with their professional hat on, say, 'I may not know you but I have very good instincts and can tell in a moment who is telling me the truth and who is lying. That's why I'm good at my job, and I believe in you!' But that didn't seem to be anyone's priority.

The hearing was starting on time but Matt couldn't sit with us. He had to go into the dock and join the other defendants. I had forgotten that and felt very sad and disappointed to see my husband once again escorted by a security guard. We went into the court room and this time the dock was directly behind us. When Matt went in he was the last to arrive. Jennifer Thornton was already there, looking very smart and very different from last week. Mr and Mrs Carter, Brian Dorfmann and Dave Edwards sat there looking impassively in front of them.

I wish I could write and say that Neil Harvey really knew his stuff and that we were all in and out of the court in no time at all. But if you're following the pattern of this case you'll realize before I even write the words that this wasn't so as Mr Harvey, although probably a good solicitor, had completely under-estimated the court hearing. From the moment the same awful, mumbling prosecuting solicitor began to read from his notes, any fool could tell that this was a case brought by the Crown with the National Crime Squad partnering them. The same detectives were there, all grinning together, but this time the judge took charge and actually appeared to be more approach-able than the magistrate the week before. After nearly three hours of endless nit-picking, haggling and trying to get as many points as possible over the defence team, the prosecution threw a major spanner in the works by telling the judge they wanted Jennifer Thornton's and Matt Davidson's bail revoked! The butterflies in my stomach began dancing round and round. I couldn't believe it was possible. We all listened in sheer disbelief as, talk about wanting it all their own way, the Crown Prosecution also wanted the case to be heard in Bristol.

I held my breath for what seemed an age before the judge spoke and thank goodness his decision went against the Crown. Logistically Bristol was out of the question. It could be a long case resulting in a trial that might last a number of months. Legal teams, defendants and witnesses couldn't be expected to travel such a long way when they all lived in London; therefore the case would be handed across to a south London Crown Court.

'With reference to the two defendants, Mr Davidson and Miss Thornton, I see no reason why I should change their bail conditions; they have all sureties in place. Therefore Mr Davidson's and Miss Thornton's bail stands.'

'Thank you, Judge,' I said out loud, not caring who could hear me! The judge was the one rational person in the court. Lawyers, liars! How easily you can get those two words mixed up?

What a horrible business to be in, doing your damnedest to persuade a judge to lock up someone as honest as Matt and by all accounts throw away the key until it was felt he had suffered enough!

'I can tell you something, Geoff; they are not doing this because Matt's a threat to society. I believe that bastard Clarke wants all six defendants shoved in custody, like a neat little package for him, whilst he plays around with people's lives and plans his ghastly tactics. Well he's not going to ruin our lives!'

'He doesn't know you at all, Claire! At least he didn't get his way with the judge, no matter what the prosecution said!'

Alex Landers was on his mobile when we came out of the court room so we were unable to engage him in any conversation. He just signalled to us, 'I'll be in touch with Mr Harvey and safe journey home.'

I was very relieved to see my husband talking to Mr Travers, who looked quite shaken himself. Matt thanked him for just being there, even though through no fault of his own he was unprepared and unequipped to have helped Matt if the unthinkable had happened and the judge had agreed with the Crown Prosecution. Mr Travers had no case notes and would have had to try and bluff his way in court, no thanks to Neil Harvey for not being there himself, and for presuming that this was just a simple hearing. Even from our limited knowledge of the case, it was all far from simple!

We couldn't wait to get out of the court and drive away from Bristol as quickly as possible. We stopped off at a motorway services and ate the best fish and chips we had ever tasted. I'm sure if we had only drunk bottled water it would have been as good as champagne – just knowing that Matt wouldn't be returning to that prison and wouldn't have to go to court in Bristol was worth celebrating, especially when a Crown Court in south London was taking over the case! For now we smiled, we laughed and we thought stuff the lot of them! Tomorrow's another day and we'll see what happens...

Our short-lived celebration turned into a mammoth event lasting almost five horrible years. The very bumpy ride rapidly progressed into a series of high-flying twists and turns, and cat and mouse games. You can liken it to a fairground – and I don't mean your local park where you can have family fun knocking down coconuts, eating candyfloss and taking a gentle ride on a roundabout! I'm talking about the scariest, highest roller coaster that works its way very slowly to the top and races down at such a high speed that you hang on for dear life in case you fall over the edge! And you know the people around you feel the same because their screams can be heard miles away.

This is not a textbook and I haven't written a sermon. This is the state of play in true life that can damage any one of us at any given time. Because of the lengthy time factor of this case, which has the honour of being acknowledged as the longest prosecution case ever, I wrote notes as it went along, explaining how it continued to run and run. You'll read a shortened version that invites you to be part of our lives through this awful ordeal, but not on a daily basis I hasten to add. Just enough for you to get a feeling of what Matt and the Davidson family had to deal with.

12

After spending a relatively quiet weekend, Matt decided his first port of call was to go and see Philip Taylor, the senior partner at the firm of accountants where Matt was a subcontractor. We couldn't keep on saying Matt was ill so Mr Taylor needed to be told the truth. An appointment was made that Monday at 11 a.m. I offered to go with Matt for moral support, as Taylor wasn't what I call a 'people person'. I was surprised when Matt said yes.

But what was even more surprising was Philip Taylor's reaction to Matt. As we parked the car we saw him waiting outside the building. Instead of beckoning us to come in, he came over and said, 'Let's talk in here.' Matt told him what had happened, but without pause for thought Taylor suggested a cooling-off period.

'Let's put water between us and when this all blows over you can always return.' This meant handing back the company car, although Mr Taylor said we could have two weeks' grace to organize another car.

'How very generous of him!' I said sarcastically to Matt as we drove home. 'I never liked him anyway and you can go forward now, because I know how clever you are. Most of Taylor's clients liked you more than him anyway, so don't worry. It will be all right.'

'I'm not that worried, Claire, but it was rather brutal. It seemed as though he already knew what had happened and had made a judgment.'

'Yes, I always thought he was small-minded. Never give

people like that a second thought. He's definitely not worth it, so we'll just cross him off our Christmas card list.'

Within a few days, clients of Matt at the office asked for our number and very slowly his practice began to build up. Putting two fingers up to Taylor, we were able to arrange a three-year lease of a brand new car very quickly through a kind builder client who was happy to help. So one evening before the end of the two-week timescale, we drove the old company car to the office, parked it outside the front door, put the keys in an envelope and posted it through the letterbox. We never saw Taylor again.

We visited Neil Harvey's office in the City twice. The first time, in the middle of May, we waited ages for him to arrive as he had been delayed at court, so we hardly had a meeting with him at all. On top of that we had a lovely parking ticket too! The second time, in June, was definitely not a good meeting. Neil Harvey had been given a load of lever arch files from the Crown Prosecution and an audio tape. It turned out the Crime Squad had bugged the Carters' house for years. We went into the board room, which was a lower ground room without a window; it was stiflingly hot. Harvey was laughing with a young clerk. He put his feet up on the board room table and ate a banana whilst listening to the tape of muffled voices, which he thought was very funny. I found his remarks hurtful and unnecessary. The voices did sound a bit like the Daleks from *Dr Who*, but the solicitor roaring with laughter made us feel very uncomfortable. He spoke about the Carter family and my husband as though Matt wasn't even in the room. It was aggravating, to say the least. I looked at Matt and, although usually good at hiding his emotions, I knew him well enough to see he wasn't happy.

By September we had been recommended to another solicitor practising criminal law. On the surface Jack Sandler appeared to be very friendly and personable and he talked Matt's language – football. Again neither of us knew one criminal solicitor from another so we could only go by word of mouth. This solicitor was a good talker, he had a very clear, concise voice and he told us about cases he and a barrister friend had won together. The barrister wasn't a QC but we were assured he knew how to handle fraud cases and that Matt's situation should be easy for him to take on board. At this early stage we didn't want to ask the solicitor about the cases they had lost together.

So it was arranged that Matt and I would go to Blackfriars Court and answer questions on the stand in front of the trial judge who would be in charge of the Carter case. Paul was very understanding when Matt told him he was grateful for the initial recommendation, 'but, four months down the line, I don't feel as though I've moved forward at all. I'm not comfortable with Neil Harvey, and although I'm sure Alex Landers is a good, competent barrister it doesn't feel right for me. I need to have faith and confidence in the team, and I don't have any.'

The Crown Court at Blackfriars is a modern building in an area completely unfamiliar to us. We left our house in north London at 7.30 a.m. and drove across the City, which took ages. With only ten minutes to spare before we were called, we managed to find a place to park by some disused railway arches now being utilized as parking space. On a dark, dreary winter's day it was quite a scary place to drive into; machine guns and spats would not have seemed out of place and your imagination could work in overdrive.

The court didn't appear too intimidating owing to the modern décor; that is, until you noticed the bewigged and black-robed male and female barristers walking through the lengthy corridors. I'm sure if you saw any of them outside the court wearing denims, without all the paraphernalia, they wouldn't look quite so imposing. As it was, they were like actors waiting to take centre stage, all dressed for the part. I hoped ours had learned his lines!

At least the security men and women waiting near the revolving front doors seemed friendly enough. The whole process of changing Matt's legal counsel took about thirty minutes. The judge appeared to approve of Jack Sandler and Edward Miles, the barrister. Reading in between the lines it appeared he knew them quite well. I suppose in reality a court is like a club where all judges and prosecution and defence lawyers know one another.

To be fair to both Neil Harvey and Alex Landers, who sat in the court listening to Matt and me, they were very decent afterwards, wishing Matt good luck. Who knows whether Matt might have been too hasty in his decision to change? Sometimes it's better the devil you know, and although I had agreed with my husband in theory, we didn't know in practice yet if this new team would be any more successful! Only time would tell and this time Matt had to believe they would turn up trumps. For his sake!

It only took a few weeks and I began to worry inwardly. Just little signs told me all was not how we had hoped it would be. After our initial meeting the barrister Edward Miles, who spoke in a very soft voice, made it clear that I couldn't attend any further meetings with Matt as I was a witness. Really what he was saying was 'Claire Davidson, butt out!'

All the lever arch files had been offloaded to Jack Sandler's office from Neil Harvey. We needed to make a few trips to collect as many files as possible and still there was an overflow, so a van brought the rest to us. There was a vast amount of paperwork prepared by the National Crime Squad and the CPS for us to read and digest, although, quite honestly, we felt more like shoving it in the nearest dustbin. The enormity of the task ahead, reading pages and pages of words that meant absolutely nothing to us, was quite daunting. At the same time as all these files were arriving, the leading members of the prosecution team had withdrawn from the case, with junior counsel following very close behind. We were told the reason was that they didn't feel there was enough evidence against Mr Carter to justify a case, especially one the police had portrayed as being 'the case of the century'.

This all sounded very hopeful to Matt and me, but we were instantly brought back to earth with a bang as we were informed that a new team was already in place and that the leading counsel was far more devious than any member of the original team. Apparently he was just the ticket for the National Crime Squad to work with, and we were given the distinct impression that he would sell his old grandmother down the river if necessary for him to win. In other words, whatever was put in front of him became do-able, and, even if it didn't make any sense to anyone else, by the time Elliott Taylor was finished with the case notes it would all be easily understood, at least by the other lawyers.

'I wonder if he's related to Philip Taylor? They both seem as though they are tarred with the same brush.'

'Taylor is quite a common name, Claire, so I doubt it very much.'

Jack Sandler continued on the surface to be a very accommodating solicitor, inviting both of us to come in and have an informal chat. Before you jump to the wrong conclusion, that Matt and I were glued to one another, you couldn't be more mistaken. But if you are lucky enough to be married to your best friend, and he happens to be in the worst kind of trouble, you give each other support. Matt and I would support each other no matter what!

To get back to Mr Sandler, his opening words were usually about the Premier League, as he knew Matt would psychologically relax talking about football. Then he would hit us with alarming facts regarding the case when Matt was off-guard and imagining Jack was a trusted football friend. It was a bit like, 'Wham! In your face, pal, here are the bare facts!'

'Sorry, Matt, enough meaningless small talk. This case has a new prosecution team, and they have a great deal to catch up with, reading all the case notes. The trial originally set for early January, which I add would have put all the defence teams at a disadvantage because we too have to familiarize ourselves with loads of files, listen to audio tapes and so on, has therefore been delayed until September 2004. In one way this could be a good thing, as it gives us time to prepare your case, but there is always a flip side and, on the other side of the coin, the court won't allow you to go on holiday abroad between now and the trial.'

The room was silent as we tried to digest this information. I thought it all sounded extremely sinister and that poor Matt was going to feel completely trapped.

'Jack, I realize Matt's passport is with the police, but we didn't think Dangerous Davidson was such a threat to the public that we couldn't take a long weekend to a European city, perhaps Rome, if we asked the court politely just to have his passport on loan for three days?'

'I'm sorry, Claire. This is a criminal case and these are the rules. I realise it must be hard for you to understand but if you were determined to go abroad it could be quite a considerable amount of money to pay the court for paper-work they have to do, probably in the region of £5,000. Why would you pay such a large sum just to retrieve your passport when your holiday may cost you much less?'

'Will I be allowed to leave the house at all and go to any hotels in England?'

'Not exactly anywhere, no. Unless they are places you frequent. I would limit those to just a couple, so that if I ask the court's permission they might make a special allowance for you.'

'We visit Bournemouth where our friends have a hotel and I have a client in the north of England who owns a pretty B & B. It's not far from the place where we stayed in 2001 when Clarke phoned us and told us to get on with our lives.'

Sandler ignored Matt's remark. 'If you have the addresses with you, give them to my PA Marianne and she will lodge them. But you won't be able to decide to go on a spontaneous whim late on a Friday night. You will have to tell Marianne by a typed fax five working days before.'

He looked at us as though he was kindness itself, but I couldn't quite trust him. For Matt's sake, though, I smiled politely and we thanked him for his time.

That's how we lived. As often as we could we escaped from London and spent time with Kate and Keith or by the lake in the north.

October was spent reading files and writing to anyone I hoped would take notice. This included the Blair regime and Number 10, Downing Street's Communication Department, though why they were called Communication for the life of me I didn't know. First of all I received a standard piece of illiterate rubbish calling me 'Mr Claire' and fobbing me off in such a way that you could see they hadn't read the content of my letter at all. So much for the Prime Minister! We received a much better response from our local MP. He made an appointment to see us and was very amicable and kindly, taking the time to listen to Matt. He said he would look into the case in more detail, and within a few days he wrote a very encouraging letter stating that he believed Matt Davidson had done nothing wrong at all, and that hopefully it would be just a matter of time before the charges against him were dropped. This was the first positive response.

I became square-eyed as I spent so much time looking up organizations on the computer who could help regarding a miscarriage of justice. I received a few helpful replies by email. One was a very lengthy one from a totally disillusioned ex policewoman, who gave me some very sound advice and told me to fight for my husband, not to sit back and trust in the legal system. She kindly pointed me to an organization in the north of England called INNOCENT. They held meetings in the form of a discussion group, so I arranged to attend one, and I was immediately drawn to the people sitting around the table. It's hard to imagine the suffering they had been put through!

The meeting was made up of people who sadly had close members of their families stuck behind bars for crimes they hadn't committed. I sat there listening whilst they openly poured their hearts and guts out to me. I was completely baffled and sickened to my stomach. These people were lovely: They were genuine, decent people suffering day in, day out, and each story became more horrific. I told them about Matt and said I would bring my mother-in-law to a meeting. Maybe Helen would relate to a couple of women of her age group, as they rightly pointed out that our circumstances were different. We were fighting at the very beginning, whereas they were all trying to fight after the inevitable had already happened, and for some it was too late.

I contacted a wonderful psychic in Southend-on-Sea. I know the many sceptics out there will laugh at this, but it worked for me. I don't want to preach about it, but if you are faced with a make or break threatening situation that suddenly takes control of your life, all I can say is if you keep an open mind anything is possible. Linda Dawkins had been one hundred per cent accurate when I'd gone to see her for the first time in 2001. I had been recommended to her through three New Zealand nurses who were involved in my aftercare following my spinal operations. I told them the horrible surgeon had said I wouldn't survive, and they all said that was rubbish – and much more about the surgeon who performed the operations that I cannot put into print! They suggested I see Linda, as they had and she'd been spot on with them. Linda turned out to be the real deal, extremely gifted, and she'd told me I would be fine and to get death out of my head. She'd gone on to tell me things about Matt's childhood that I would never have known, and when I'd played the tape to him he'd been amazed she'd been so accurate. Although up until that time he'd been quite sceptical, he actually made an appointment to see her and came away with the same conclusion as I did. She is one remarkable lady. So, it made sense to see her now as Matt seemed to be going round in circles and getting nowhere fast. Linda said immediately, 'Matt's completely innocent. They all know it and he will never go to trial. He will definitely come out of it, although it will seem to take forever. A trial won't happen.' These words were a complete tonic to Matt, Helen, Sam and me and throughout the sorry saga she kept our hopes alive. She's an absolute gem and we feel lucky to know her.

As well as Linda we had a great network of friends. Let's face it, when you are as down as we were, true friends are a test and if you have them, hold on to them. Our friends really helped us through the many dark days and, believe me, there were many. Carol and Mike were so supportive. We gave them regular updates over dinner, and we were always cheered up as they saw things in a different way to us. Their point of view was very valuable.

Kate and Keith will never know nor perhaps understand how we looked forward to driving to Bournemouth on a Friday evening, once Jack Sandler's secretary Marianne had written to the court requesting their permission to let Matt sleep at a different address for two nights, and she had eventually faxed us with the court's consent. It seemed such a lengthy, ridiculous and around the houses procedure. Sometimes we wouldn't get the fax until mid-afternoon, so we were like children, excited about our weekend adventure and packing our overnight bag quickly. Bournemouth became our place to unwind and be with friends, who knew us well and laughed at Matt's account of what had been said to him at legal meetings. As Kate pointed out, knowing Matt, anyone could see it was all a load of rubbish. By the time we left them to drive back to London we felt temporarily happier and more positive, until we arrived back at Helen's and saw how many files had been dumped in the hallway, the lounge and in the garage. It might have all been nonsense, but it was a nonsense that seemed to make sense to Detective Chief Inspector Clarke and the new leading light for the prosecution Elliott Taylor.

We shortened his name to ET, but he wasn't a loveable character such as the film director Steven Spielberg would have made everyone love. No, this ET could definitely go home and stay there. He and Clarke were not at all pleasant personalities and although we had not yet seen this ET, the image we conjured up in our minds was quite a ghastly-looking character. At some stage soon we knew we would find out for ourselves, when it became time to attend the court in south London for the hearing.

With all of this in mind and lever arch files to plough through, we were kept very busy. Matt's practice was growing with recommendations, most of the people having no idea what Matt was going through. When we planned our little weekend trips they would say, 'Are you away again? Lucky you! You do enjoy life!' Little did they know ...

When we were granted permission to travel north and stay by the lake, we would ask Marianne to ask the court for an extra day so we could stay until Monday. Then we would have time to see another couple of friends who were the first holiday mates we had gelled with and really liked. Our Italian trip to Lake Garda was the last time we had been abroad, and Sylvia and Charlie, who lived in Wigan, had joined in Matt's birthday celebrations. Charlie is a retired police inspector, the least likely member of the 'old bill' that you could ever imagine. A gentle, kind, caring man, he dumbfounded Matt and me when he said he had dealt with all sorts of grizzly, grey areas in life. He was nothing like creepy Clarke, who never in our wildest fantasies would we have described as a kind human being. Sylvia is wonderful fun. She's a no-nonsense, get on with it, straightforward personality. When we told them about Matt's ordeal, they reacted accordingly.

Charlie gave Matt quiet advice whilst Sylvia was as angry as I was. But, as she herself said, she wasn't so contained, and her very direct northern tongue lashed out at many of the legal bods who felt themselves above the law. If push comes to shove, there are cracks in all establishments. There will always be a bent copper, a dodgy member of parliament and definitely lawyers who blot their copy book. Sylvia, if you excuse the pun, didn't take any prisoners! She took the case apart piece by piece. So Bournemouth and the north of England became our lifelines. We could leave the files and all the crap behind us in London.

However, any enjoyment we found was always short-lived. Jack Sandler would ring us as soon as we arrived back, and if he was unlucky enough to get me at the other end of the phone I would bombard him with questions. I can honestly say, hand on heart, that within a short period of time I wasn't at all sure about him. I had a nagging doubt in my mind that maybe Neil Harvey should have been given a chance.

13

Towards the end of October we went to Sandler's office to collect a few extra files that had materialized. Matt asked him out of the blue, 'How can I be dismissed from this case?'

Sandler looked at both of us rather sheepishly and said, 'You can't, I'm afraid. It's the way the current Home Secretary has issued a bill that supports the CPS. As this case has been brought by them and the National Crime Squad, you have to be very patient. Until the trial actually starts and the leading prosecution barrister has finished addressing his opening gambit to the trial judge and the jury, the defence are powerless to do anything. Eddie can then speak and ask for you to be discharged, stating that the proceedings should be stayed as an abuse of the process of the court. Then with the correct words said on your behalf, we would hope the outcome would be in your favour.'

'So, to put it in a nutshell, Matt has to sit it out for as long as it takes until a grotty trial starts? Even though he has never done anything wrong in his life?'

'Yes, Claire, I'm afraid so.'

This all appeared to go over Matt's head and I looked at my husband in horror. He seemed to have lost the plot and be under Jack Sandler's brainwashing spell. He also appeared to mistake the solicitor's carefully chosen words for a form of football-related male bonding and a weird kind of friendship.

I found it more and more frustrating as I could see that the longer the case was drawn out, and the further Matt was sucked in, the more the solicitor and his cronies would be laughing all the way to the bank. Whenever we came out of a meeting, and there were quite a few in October, Matt would say, 'He's a friendly guy,' or words to that effect. I thought it was too soon for me to put a spoke in the wheel, but I had a strong feeling there was a great deal going on in the Carter case that Joe Public would never know.

Both our birthdays are in October, but neither of us felt in the mood to celebrate. Early November was our silver anniversary, though, so we asked if we could spend it in the north of England. This time we made a special request to stay in a plush hotel with all the amenities in the centre of Manchester. You may wonder why we yet again wanted to go north. There are many beautiful locations in England we could choose from: we could have stayed in London at a hotel in Park lane and been near all the West End theatres, or visited Devon and Cornwall and the glorious countryside there. But we didn't choose the location; the court indirectly did. Together, Matt and I could only go to Bournemouth, Dorset or Hollingworth Lake, not far from Manchester. Mr Sandler pointed out that the paperwork wouldn't be too difficult to achieve if we were only going a few miles away from where we normally stayed. I couldn't see his logic at all, though, and I hope when you read this you'll agree.

During our anniversary dinner in the hotel, the concierge informed Matt that there was a fax coming through for him. It was one page and very much to the point, from Jack Sandler.

Happy Anniversary,

Hope you're enjoying the break. I am writing to inform you that the new prosecution team have decided, for want of a better expression, to drop Brian Dorfmann and David Edwards from the Carter case. They are no longer needed as the case is costing the public a great deal of money.

Call me when you get back.

Jack.

Matt passed the fax over to me without saying anything. I needed to read it over and over again before I could digest Sandler's words. I think you could see the smoke clouding our table as we were both seething.

'Matt, why do you think they are allowed to walk free and not you? It's disgusting, unreal, unfair. Clarke needs his badge torn off and thrown in the rubbish bin, and how dare Sandler write this fax to you when he knows you are trying to enjoy a few days away? He's sitting on the fence, by the sound of it. He didn't need to write this to you; he could have waited for you to see him at the end of the week and told you this exciting news tactfully. You'll have to ask him why, why and why.'

'Okay, Claire, calm down. We're never going to understand this bloody law, but I want a full explanation of how these two men can be dismissed just like that! After six months, and I can't! It's beyond comprehension!'

'When we get back, Matt, you have a meeting with new clients and your diary is pretty full, so I'm going to read as many files as possible one by one, every word, every line, and see what I can understand from this case. One of the things I don't understand is the bug put in Adrienne and Matthew Carter's house for so long. How can that be legal?'

Our dinner had a bittersweet taste after that news and we spent the next day in a dark mood. It was actually a relief to go back home for once; at least we were hands on in London. There was a copy letter sent to us from the Crown, confirming a September 2004 trial and that there would now be four defendants.

The following day Jack Sandler telephoned and said we should both see him at his office that afternoon. He was very matter of fact about the two defendants who were dismissed. 'Yes, they were lucky; even their counsel thought so. But now it means the case has changed direction, and is similar to Al Capone and his tax case.'

'What you are saying, Jack, is that the Crime Squad didn't do their homework! They assumed, quite wrongly, they would be able to get witnesses on board to testify against Mr Carter, and I bet not one single witness has come forward. So, between Martin Clarke and Elliott Taylor they've had to make dramatic changes. Obviously, personally I have nothing against Mr Dorfmann and Mr Edwards. I don't know them at all, so I cannot judge their character one way or the other. But it's obvious that Clarke couldn't make anything stick!'

'I wouldn't be sure of that, Matt. We don't know the reason.'

'Oh really, Jack, do you think we have just come from the funny farm and you can spin Matt a good story that will just be accepted? Everything you've said smells to high heaven. This is now a tax case, so how convenient to have an obliging individual like Matt, who also happens to be an accountant, who the prosecution can shove into the centre of the loop, just like the picture hook holding up the frame. If the court were to let him go, the bloody picture would fall apart and this mammoth, brilliant intelligence case would become null and void. Obviously six defendants were too many, but four would be very manageable! Matt may have been the Carters' accountant for a while, but what about the accountant before him, and the one after him? Why has my husband been given the short straw?'

'He hasn't been given the short straw, Claire. Matt's voice is on one of the bugged tapes.'

'Oh of course that would make him as guilty as hell! And I must be the Bonnie to Matt's Clyde, as my voice must be on tape too. I used to visit the Carter house when Sam was with Jazmin. Bloody hell! That makes our daughter a number one suspect as well, because her conversations with Jazmin must have been recorded! And the postman, the baker, the candlestick maker! Any delivery person, friends, family, plus the telephone and the television for God's sake!'

Jack Sandler in reply simply blinked at us over the rim of his glasses, and pushed his hand through his hair. Meeting Sandler today was a mistake; we were going round in circles and Sandler was getting on my nerves big time!

'I'm sorry you both feel this way about the case, but it's out of our control and we have to deal with it accordingly. So I suggest you begin reading the files, Matt, and highlighting points you wish to make.'

From that moment, there was mutual dislike between Jack Sandler and me.

Matt spent a couple of days reading through files and offloading some to me, but in between he had to see clients and carry on as normally as possible. He was quite remarkable really, as he was able to throw himself into his work and not be fazed by the dreadful task in front of him. I was taking as much off his shoulders as was possible, and he trusted me to become a Jane Marple until I learnt the truth, so I spent a great deal of time reading files that were boring and had absolutely nothing to do with my husband I thought it was time to go wherever was necessary and Helen said she would come with me.

First of all I collected as much information about the case and put Matt's situation on paper. We went to the Court of Human Rights in Strasbourg, France, taking the papers I had documented, along with the many questions that were unanswered, that were necessary nit-picking questions the police, lawyers and government wouldn't expect a member of the general public to ask. You are supposed to accept what is dumped on you and suffer the consequences quietly. Why?

When we returned we travelled to the north of England for a couple of days as there was an INNOCENT meeting. Helen listened, as I had, to the many sad cases that people were helpless to do anything constructive about once a member of their family had been fitted up and banged up.

I carried on writing to everyone I could think of, but without success. Then my computer began crashing. It was obviously being hacked and my letters being read by the powers that be. This was beyond me! Why would my letters and questions cause such an internal problem amongst the bodies behind this case?

INNOCENT were part of a large Miscarriages of Justice Forum being held in Manchester at the end of the month. I travelled from London and arrived at the packed hall just before the first speaker stood up on the stage. I sat with people I could see had issues, sadness, grief, and no one to turn to. Speakers took it in turn to offer their valued advice. I sat there writing notes. It was life changing, listening to some of the people who had suffered at first hand, being locked up as an Innocent but portrayed as guilty. The audience were allowed to ask questions; they shared their own horrendous stories, and when I write horrendous, that's what I mean! A young son of eighteen had hanged himself in his cell through false imprisonment; another had died of a heart attack through lies, accusations and police forging statements; and it went on and on! I felt sick to my stomach. It didn't sound as though help was available – and one of the speakers, who commanded a great deal of air time on the stage, quite frankly should have been booed off. He spouted carefully rehearsed rubbish that only a complaints department relating to the police could get away with! It was a bureaucratic load of old claptrap!

After almost an hour of losing the will to live and judging by others' expressions that they felt the same, an inspirational forensic criminologist stood up. He was an incredible orator. I was transfixed, as he shouted at the top of his voice to everyone.

'Get off your behinds and do something constructive! What's the point of simply belonging to organizations? Sure, you meet others in similar situations, you share your stories, you make soothing noises to each other, drink tea, eat biscuits and go away feeling flat and often even more depressed. But what do you actually achieve? Nothing! The thugs in blue, and more often than not in plain clothes, come at dawn and rip your home apart. Nothing sinks into the person they have arrested and the family are in shock. At the police station, the policeman isn't listening to you and doesn't want to listen to you. None of it makes any sense at all, but it all begins to dawn on you that the cops are not interested one little bit. All they want is a result! The case is so full of holes it's a cross between Swiss cheese and a watering can!

'In court your appointed barrister doesn't ask the questions that you want raised; and all the reassuring noises your solicitor makes are said only for effect, nothing more. You have been fitted up by a policeman looking for promotion and a miscarriage of justice stems solely from that. The Crown Prosecution should be stopping all the false allegations coming to court, and the waste of millions of pounds of public money, but do they? Of course they bloody don't! So, we live in a fit-up system. The biggest crime is the government knowing that people who are innocent are being put into a web of lies to support a dodgy case but continuing to allow it. All the authorities work together. The police want the result. The Crown Prosecution want the good exciting case. There is a league table, and perjury is what they deal with, so the Crown aren't worried in the slightest whether you are innocent or not! They have the means to fit you in the frame by changing notes and simply duffing you up! Then it becomes an official fit-up! Sometimes there doesn't even have to be a crime! Just a few police to say you did whatever they say you did! No one is interested in getting the truth; all they aim for is the result!

'We have to keep fighting individual cases and get people heard. You cannot afford to wait for the solicitor specializing in criminal cases to pull his finger out! Nine times out of ten you will find yourself behind bars for no reason at all, other than a promotion for the boys in blue. At the house of the dawn raid, if there is no evidence found when checking files, cupboards, drawers at the defendant's home, then quite frankly there is no evidence. The policeman who swears on oath and then lies is committing perjury and should serve a prison sentence. Remember, these are all important lessons to learn. There will always be miscarriages of justice until someone takes notice. Every effort must be made from the very start to demolish the false evidence that both police and prosecution have conjured up together. Signatures can be falsified and vital documents are often destroyed or deleted. The police have various destruction policies, but police paperwork can and always should be re-examined for flaws before any trial commences. You can lobby members of the European Parliament if necessary and you are not getting the support you require from your own country. Finally, make sure your solicitor researches activities of the relevant crime squad and the prosecution. You have a right to obtain past disciplinary offences of police and the prosecuting team. The Crown Prosecution are the bully boys for this wonderful justice system. They will produce a million pieces of paper or tape recordings and most of it is hardly relevant, but it all helps them pad out a case and convict an innocent person. Many years ago well-known crooks and hardened criminals were the major targets quite correctly being fitted up. That was when we had a good, honourable law! Now it's the middle classes, the decent men and women on the street, who are being targeted! Participate as much as possible in your defence. Remember, you cannot afford to lose. Your solicitor still goes home, if you lose; you don't!'

Wow! I was mesmerized, as were others in the rows of seats around me. He could have been speaking to Matt and me, and I'm sure the few hundred people in the hall felt the same way. There was nothing to add after his triumphant speech so I travelled back to London with a new burst of energy and even more determination to campaign for Matt.

14

By Christmas I had read through a number of files, each one more meaningless than the ones I had read before. Christmas came and went in an uneventful blur. Jack Sandler was off to some exotic resort and so was Edward Miles. We didn't mind not going abroad as we always enjoyed Christmas in Bournemouth, but Sandler appeared oblivious to Matt's predicament and even in the middle of a serious conversation about forensic accounting he would give a throwaway line that held no interest whatsoever for Matt and me about what a wonderful lunch he'd had last Sunday at his favourite restaurant in the south of France. He just hopped over for the weekend and who should be at the next table with his family? Mark Ronson, Jennifer Thornton's barrister.

'Aren't you fortunate, Jack, that you didn't have to ask the court's permission to go to France for lunch? And now the Bahamas? What a sad life you lead!' I don't think he even recognized the sarcasm in my remark.

January, February and March 2004 were spent at endless court hearings. The first in early January was quite an eye-opener. It was so strange to see 'Matt Davidson Court 6' on an electronic naming format. It just hit home to me, every word the forensic criminologist had said. Defendant Davidson was being truly fitted up by England's finest justice system.

The Carters were there with their team but we merely acknowledged each other. Jennifer Thornton did the same, and if you can visualize four defendants each with solicitor, senior and junior defence barristers and clerks, plus the

Crime Squad, at least four of them, and a team of prosecuting barristers, you'll understand that this case was indeed costing a bloody fortune.

I went to a very clinical, though hygienic ladies room, and when I returned I found Matt sitting on a bench in a corner of the foyer looking very angry.

'What's happened?'

'Bloody Clarke, that's what happened! I was reading the notice board when he came and stood next to me. He actually asked me if I knew what court we were all in! I don't know if he thought I was going to spend time having a polite friendly conversation with him, but it didn't happen! I blanked him and walked away without saying a word. The creep looked bewildered and just stood there like an idiot, not able to understand the board's numbering system. What planet are these guys on if they think they can ruin your life and that you'll respect them! He's a piece of work!'

'Well, you know what I believe, Matt. What comes around goes around. He'll suffer one day, wait and see! Look at the comedy duo over there! Jack Sandler and Elliott Taylor chatting as though they are the best of buddies. I know you are the one who is directly living through this hell, but please keep your eyes open and be aware of what's going on around you. Sandler and ET remind me of a cross between the hunky, sexy characters from The Odd Couple – Felix and Oscar, played brilliantly by Jack Lemmon and Walter Matthau. ET and Sandler are not as talented though!'

The comedy made light of the serious situation until Matt's junior barrister came over. Rupert Dunne seemed a pleasant enough young man, and after making brief small talk he told Matt he needed to go into a conference room with him, where Edward Miles and Jack Sandler would brief him on the morning's events.

It was all very unreal, the entire set up. Each defendant went off with their counsel to small allotted conference rooms next to Court 6, and I began the patient waiting process of sitting outside writing notes, snippets of conversations, anything I could glean. Once everyone was told to go into court I sat outside alone. After a while barristers would walk past from different cases and ask me, 'Who are you? Are you a journalist?'

I would just smile or say, 'I'm sure you'll find out one day!'

In April at Easter, Helen, her sister Laura and her brother-in-law Leslie were invited to visit their younger brother in Spain. Sam no longer lived with us. She was sharing a flat with a dancer and it was obviously better for her in many ways. It was right that she wanted her independence, and although she had paid a visit to meet Mr Sandler she was as unimpressed with him as I was. We were glad she wasn't in the thick of it all and therefore not directly involved, and although she spoke to us every day we tried to keep the conversation as light as possible. It didn't seem fair to tell Sam all the horrible dirty dealings, although we knew when we saw her that Matt would update her in his own inimitable understated fashion, which was better as he wasn't as scathing as I would be. So, with Helen out of the house, it was very quiet and we took the opportunity of reading through the glorious files without being interrupted.

Easter Monday had been a particularly quiet day and Matt had just gone out for a short while to put petrol in the car. We were meeting friends for dinner that night, and travelling back and forth to the South London Court lately meant the tank was very low.

I was in my own little world, trying to imagine better times, as I was plodding through an extra heavy file with the bold letter 'A' on the front cover and an explanation page telling me the following pages were taped conversations between Mr Carter and his colleagues, and also personal conversations among the Carter family.

If I had been Adrienne Carter I would have been distraught

and horrified to see in print personal domestic squabbles being highlighted across the page for any Joe Shmo to gloat over. And if this was intelligence information of a high and dangerous calibre, why had the police bothered to spend time taping the frightening fact that Matthew Carter had a bad cold and felt rotten? After that piece of trivia, inconsistent pages followed. There was a very aggressive argument between Mr Carter and Mr X, which quite frankly reminded me of a scene from *The Godfather* film, as there were American slang words and phrases I felt sure a London cockney would never use! And, although I cannot swear to it because I wasn't there, it seemed highly likely that they had also recorded Mr Carter watching DVDs.

Anyway, the phone ringing broke into my thoughts. I never expected to hear, completely out of the blue, the voice at the end of the line, that of Adrienne Carter! It was a brief but friendly call to let us know they were changing their representation. She said if Matt was unhappy with his team he might also like to change to their new counsel. I must have sounded like a dithering old biddy because I was completely stunned to hear her voice. Eventually I think I said, 'I hope your new team work out for you, but I think Matt is okay with the team he has at the moment. What made you decide to change? Gerald Harris seemed very pro-fessional and you appeared to be getting on famously together!'

'Yes, we liked him as a person but we didn't like the advice he was giving us and what he expected my husband to do. Matthew has been legitimate for years, and so this new team were recommended to us. They are Greek Cypriots, extremely friendly people, and we feel very hopeful with them.'

'Thank you for the call and I wish you luck.'

Matt was as surprised as I had been when I told him Adrienne Carter rang. 'Greek guys? Well, I'm okay with Jack, Eddie and Rupert. I know you're not keen and don't trust them, but it's their job and the way the law works, so for the moment I shall give them the benefit of the doubt.'

Within a week of Adrienne's call another hearing was scheduled. It was only going to be for an hour, as it was simply introducing the new Carter representation to the judge. Geoff rang to say he had some time on his hands. As the court was only a short ride away on his bike, we arranged to meet there at 9 a.m. the following Monday morning.

Geoff was his upbeat self when he greeted us and was very interested in meeting Matt's team, although I didn't feel Jack Sandler would have been interested in meeting him! We all sat in the court canteen as the hearing had been delayed for a while and watched intrigued as Adrienne and Matthew Carter came in with their new solicitors and counsel. It was all very friendly and you could be excused for thinking it wasn't a court, but a friendly gathering of minds for a morning's worth of chitchat! Both Jack and Eddie knew Matthew Carter's solicitor Costas, and they had vaguely heard of Adrienne Carter's solicitor, who worked with Costas at the same practice. She was called Androula. Mr Carter in his very generous way wanted to buy coffee and tea for everyone, although, as the hearing was about to start, we all went down, this time to Court 5, and as usual I sat outside.

Within a very short time, everyone came out. The deed had been done and the judge hadn't seemed to have any objections to the change of representation. Time was very short, though, as it was early May, and Costas and co had been granted extra time to read all the files. They were after all the leading counsel as the Carters were defendants one and two, with Jennifer Thornton third and Matt Davidson last. Therefore the trial that had been originally set for January 2004 and put back to September 2004 was again delayed until January 2005!

Geoff came out of the court room grinning and talking animatedly. He seemed to find it all very interesting. On our way to the car park we stopped at a coffee shop and Matt and Geoff discussed the situation. I listened intently to Geoff's words of wisdom; he appeared to be fascinated with the situation all round, the case, the Carters; he had a point of view on everyone and everything! ET and his prosecution team had all turned up like a little army, together with two men from Clarke's National Crime unit. Geoff had a great deal to say about all of them too, including Jack Sandler, but he seemed to reserve his judgement on Edward Miles. Geoff said he would go with Matt to the next meeting at his barrister's chambers so that he could see what progress was being made, if any! During Geoff's interpretation on court procedure, fact finding and what he thought about the trial being put back for another eight months, Matt just listened and laughed. Geoff when taking centre stage could be very funny.

A couple of weeks later I met a retired Scandinavian judge through a friend of mine. I showed him some of the documents and the first thing he said was, 'What is your husband's team doing to defend him exactly and why aren't they going for a dismissal? I agree with the forensic criminologist; it appears to be a setup. Go and see the solicitor and watch his reaction to the questions I'm writing down for you.'

So, armed with ammunition and completely fired up, we all went to see Jack Sandler, including Helen. My mother-in-law had heard so much about him that she wanted to see him for herself.

He had his usual chat about who were going to win the Premiership and then asked me how my meeting had gone with the retired judge! I had mentioned it to him the last time we met and was surprised he'd remembered.

'It went very well, thank you. In fact, he has given me these questions to show you, as he seems to think in the same way I do that more could be done to help Matt!'

He merely glanced at the written notes I shoved in front of

145

him. 'Claire, I have explained to both of you, my hands are tied.'

'I don't think so. I don't believe for one moment that you are doing all you can!'

He kept on blinking at me. By then I had really lost it and so I banged on his desk hard, shouting God knows what at him! In response he said, 'You are upsetting my staff. They are not used to such behaviour.'

I stormed out of his office and saw Marianne typing away. I could have sworn she had a slight grin on her face as she stared straight ahead at her computer. She didn't look at all fazed by my contretemps. As far as I was concerned it was bloody overdue anyway.

A few days later, to gain favour, Jack Sandler sent me a letter telling me to read the enclosed about the leading prosecuting barrister, Elliott Taylor. In a trial he was working on abroad, the Attorney General directing the case had used the word 'sophistry' to describe ET's way of achieving his objective.

The rest of the letter defeated the object of sending it to us in the first place, as Sandler went on to add that we might read and keep the document he'd sent, but we needed to understand that the trial judge was fully aware of the facts and that as it was a couple of years ago it wouldn't make any difference to our case. He'd just thought it was something we should know!

'Christ, Matt! It sounds as though the lawyers need to go to trial!'

The ET revelation made me even more determined to drive Matt's team mad! So much so, the next time I saw Jack Sandler he greeted me with an extra nasty grin and said, 'Claire, you're obviously keeping well? You always manage to look good, and yet you double up as the wife from hell!' It was said in fun but there was a definite meaning there. I couldn't have cared less! I would much rather be called that than be liked by such a man. I wasn't about to become subservient and accommodating just so they could have an easy ride and then watch with horror as my husband was led away for however long for a crime he didn't commit! I wasn't there to be liked! I was going to be the one person giving Sandler, Miles, Clarke, ET and co a big headache they weren't used to! My brain kept telling me that if they all had nothing to hide, they wouldn't be afraid of my questions, would they? So I could only conclude they had a huge amount to conceal, plus the big bucks they were all getting from an innocent person's misery, and they were all covering up for each other.

Geoff met us as often as possible, usually for dinner in town. We would take him to a little restaurant near Piccadilly where they served the typical English food he liked: sausages and mash. We would spend the entire evening discussing the case. Geoff would enthuse and emphasize the words, 'When the trial starts next year you will be able to really sock it to the court, Matt.'

I would always stop him and say, 'Why do you always say when there is a trial? There's that little word "if". Nothing's set in stone and anything can happen between now and January.'

He would look at me and just say, 'No, Claire, this is a huge case around Matthew Carter, so I'm sure it's a definite yes, there will be a trial. But of course Matt will come out of it with flying colours.'

The strain of it all made me question how good a friend Geoff really was to Matt. I found his objectivity hard to take! He had been very kind when Matt had his account frozen at the beginning and straight away helped us out. But Matt had repaid him over and over since then and never charged him a penny for doing his yearly accounts.

In July I thought it would be a good idea for Carol to meet Jack. After all she had supported Matt's case by coming up trumps as the main surety, and Matt agreed it was a meeting

147

that was overdue. I told Sandler to book a table near his office, which was about five minutes walk from Selfridges, and Carol and I would meet him at the restaurant. I was taking them both to lunch. He agreed immediately and lunch began quite well as he seemed suitably impressed with Carol. They both shared the wine while I kept to mineral water. I know water sounds boring, but I'm not a great wine drinker at the best of times and I needed to keep my wits in case Sandler said too much. Sure enough, after three or four glasses that's exactly what he did!

'Has Matt read many files, Claire? He must go through all of them very carefully. It's extremely necessary you get him to read them as soon as possible, do you understand what I'm saying Claire?'

I must have stared at him blankly as his usual mellifluous voice, which I thought the best thing about him, had turned harsh and ugly.

'Well, in between dealing with his clients and trying to get their accounts out, he has read quite a few files. You must understand, Jack, it's not easy when you work for yourself. I'm going through a lot of them to try and help him.'

'The only way to help him is to tell him he must read the files, and I mean all of them. He has to understand what he's been charged with. Do you want him to get six years for not knowing the answers to the questions?'

I wanted to pour the coffee over him, but as Carol was sitting opposite me he had a lucky escape.

I wanted to establish where he got the figure six from, and for what exactly? Was he saying that Matt was guilty by association and would therefore receive a penalty of six years? Or was it the drink doing too much talking? He very quickly drank his coffee, told Carol it had been lovely to meet her, thanked me briefly and said he had to rush back to his office for a meeting. He had made me feel quite ill with his throwaway, unfeeling comments.

Carol could see I was stunned. We were making a day of it and going to a beautiful art gallery before meeting Matt and Mike near Earls Court for a pizza in the evening. The wonderful lunch had gone on longer than I had anticipated and it was almost 3.30 when we came out of the restaurant. Carol suggested we go and sit down somewhere quiet where I could have a real drink. I must have looked as though I needed something to give me an instant shock-proof pick-me-up.

A couple of blocks away we arrived at the Selfridge Hotel. The lounge was very tranquil, even though we were in the heart of the West End. Thank goodness for five-star hotels in the centre of town with air conditioning, double glazing and extra comfy cushioned armchairs to simply relax in. I closed my mind to the madness that seemed to be surrounding my husband. A brandy was put in front of me and to a certain extent I managed to calm down. Carol was able to very cleverly change the subject and I left the hotel feeling far better than when I had gone in.

Meeting Matt and Mike in the evening was a good idea. Matt had also invited his client-friend Adele. She worked very near Earls Court for Colin Natali, the fabulous spinal surgeon who had taken over from the rubbish one who'd almost killed my back and me. Colin and Adele couldn't have been more supportive towards Matt. They always voiced their opinions about the case around him in very colourful terms. Adele is such an upbeat jolly soul that we were able to have a laugh, but inwardly I was petrified that my kind and caring husband, laughing at casual funny remarks, was oblivious to the fear that he was going away for a very long time. If Jack Sandler was to be believed, anyway.

15

August was quiet as the court had all gone away to wonderful warm climates. This gave Matt a chance to get on with his work and at weekends he read as many files as possible. I had started reading the 'A' file at Easter when Adrienne Carter had phoned me, and I was now trying to finish it. It was called the 'A' file as it meant audio. I would have called it the 'Argument' file, for reasons I shall explain, but I wrote brief notes as I read through this mammoth piece of alleged conversation.

There were pages and pages of family stuff, where Jazmin was having a typical daughter dispute with her parents. Domestic disagreements that every family goes through are private and not meant for a load of grubby Crime Squad to mull over. Even I felt like an intruder reading about the Carters' private home life. There were pages and pages that meant nothing to Matt. If he had no idea what they were talking about, I certainly wouldn't have a clue! Loads of words had been missed out or spelt incorrectly, so you had to make up your own sentences or at least finish the sentences they had begun! It was another example of amateurish workmanship, where no one had bothered to check their work for mistakes.

Towards the end of the file there was one line stating that Matt Davidson had taken over from the previous accountant. That was it: very short and to the point. Reading every page carefully, it was clear that Matthew Carter sometimes had friends and colleagues visit him. The transcribers had put Mr

Carter speaking to Bill, Bob, Dave, Chris, Scott, Charlie, Joe and Pete, but there wasn't one conversation between Matthew Carter and Matt Davidson, not even about the weather! Well, well, well, how very curious then to be told as part of the charges against Matt that he had taken over from Izzy Hirsch and was walking in his shoes? Why? Because he was an accountant and was just doing a normal job! What a strange, clutching at straws accusation!

Anyone with common sense would have realized that if Matt Davidson had taken over from Matthew Carter's right-hand man, or personal assistant, whatever you want to call him, surely the 'A' file would have shown a conversation between the pair of them? But there was nothing at all! It was all fantasy, a fabricated load of old hogwash, compiled by a desperate Crime Squad, prosecution and whoever else was trying to run the show. As I wrote earlier, they hadn't done their homework, and if you don't study your subject thoroughly you get very poor results.

So, with this in mind, I wrote many questions to Hugh Benedict, the trial judge. I knew I wouldn't be allowed an answer, but at least I knew my letter would be read and perhaps I had thrown a spanner in the works. Within a week I did get a reply from the court, saying that the judge had read it but couldn't write to me personally. I didn't care about that; I just wanted to let the court know we weren't going to take any old accusation lightly.

September through to the end of the year was quite a lousy time for Matt. He was juggling his work, which at that time of the year was very busy as all tax returns have to be in by 31st January. By now he had many recommendations, which was a good thing on one hand. But when all the clients started sending in their accounts together, it became daunting, especially when he was faced with a major trial. We were still hopeful that Linda was correct, but we couldn't tell Matt's counsel that our psychic advisor had reassured us there wouldn't be a trial! So Matt still went to the court to listen to ET talk endlessly. As Matt said, he loved to hear the sound of his own voice, and aren't most lawyers frustrated actors?

Then Matt started throwing up and having severe headaches. We were all very worried about him. Thankfully he was able to see his doctor very quickly. His GP listened intently to Matt's account of what was happening to him, both with his health and with the court case. I am very pleased to write that it was nothing more serious than high blood pressure, and was all stress related. Thank goodness for that! During that time even Jack Sandler had seemed to be worried about him, which I would like to think was a genuine, sincere worry on his part and not because this case was bigger than Matt Davidson and his illness could have prevented its smooth progress.

January 2005 began with a meeting in the first week at Edward Miles's chambers. It was just a briefing to go over facts and discuss how all the defence planned to proceed before the trial started. That was due to happen the following Wednesday, so the Monday and Tuesday would be spent in court with the prosecution and defence dishing out legal arguments in front of the trial judge Hugh Benedict. At the same time all the defendants' sureties had to be sworn in again, so Carol and Laura were coming with us to court on Monday. As a solicitor Paul didn't have to attend as he would be able to swear his oath at a court where he was working.

I look back and wonder how Matt ever kept his cool before a possible major trial that was alien to him. He always said he had a very clear conscience because he knew in his heart and mind that he was absolutely innocent of all charges. He believed there was still British justice and that, with the help of his defence team, he would succeed. I suppose, when you think about it, if you are the one taking centre stage, you look at the angles given to you very differently from others who are on the perimeter and can see the flaws that you can't.

However, Friday evening after going through gruelling talks with counsel, Matt suffered what we believe to be a mini breakdown. Without going into details, it was very sad to see him being put through the wringer. He is a decent human being who never had a moment's trouble in his life. Yet here he was dealing with this gigantic hurdle as though he was a robot. After that episode we knew he wasn't and it saddened Helen, Sam and me enormously to see how much he had been covering up. At some point you can only take so much and it all comes to a head. He needed to vent his feelings.

Monday morning, Carol and Laura arrived before 8 a.m. as we had to be at court by 9. Helen waved goodbye and wished Matt all the luck in the world. It must have been hard for her waiting behind to hear news, but sadly I think she was getting used to it! Sam had seen us at the weekend and had phoned Matt very early that morning, which had really cheered him up.

Matt's favourite singer of all time was the very talented Sammy Davis Jnr, and one of the tracks on a CD we had was almost worn out where we'd played it so often. It was called 'I'm Not Anyone' and had been written by Paul Anka, who also penned 'My Way 'for Frank Sinatra. Anyway, this song had words and a melody that could inspire many, and it seemed to give Matt the extra boost he needed before he went into court.

The court that Monday morning was positively heaving. There were cameramen outside and the security entrance was jam-packed. We looked at the notice board and saw the trial was scheduled to be held in Court 1. As well as the normal security who greeted everyone as they came through the revolving doors and checked bags and pockets in the same way as at any airport, two security personnel sat at a table near the court room and there was a small screen placed just in front of the court room entrance. This was apparently normal procedure whenever there was a trial of some magnitude.

When Carol and Laura were called to go in to pledge their oaths, they explained that a long screen stretched across the middle of the court, separating the dock with the defendants from the jury so that they couldn't be seen. This was in case a jury member felt intimidated by Mr and Mrs Carter, Jennifer Thornton or Dangerous Davidson! My immediate thought was what warped minds the prosecution and the police have. The screen would encourage the jurors into believing whoever sat in the dock was on a par with Jack the Ripper, Myra Hindley and Charles Manson all rolled into one!

The four defendants had all brought their sureties and there were defence barristers, solicitors and clerks all hurriedly taking their clients into conference rooms. There were journalists with their notebooks, too, and a room allocated for the prosecution together with the National Crime Squad. There was a great deal of laughter coming from that room – even that sounded evil. If you only knew my husband you would have felt for him one hundred per cent!

The four prosecuting barristers led by their number one star ET were standing in the doorway of the prosecution room. ET was showing off as usual and his number two understudy, William Channing (WC – good initials, very apt!) was grinning from ear to ear. The two other prosecutors, Tom Burns and Naomi Grossman, or Grosswoman as we lovingly called her, were pulling trolleys out of the room. They were similar to supermarket trolleys except that they were filled with files. These formed part of the prosecution evidence, which they took behind the screen and into the court.

Martin Clarke and three of his Criminal Squad all seemed to be on a high. Their inflated egos didn't really suit them. Bob Kershaw, Dick Warner and Gary Porter all reminded me of caricature, exaggerated versions of actors in *The Bill*; as for

Clarke I can't put into print what we actually thought of him and his many lies.

Jack Sandler seemed to be in his element and the leading counsel for Mr and Mrs Carter was rushing around with files. It was all very surreal.

About an hour or so later the judge was ready for all defendants, their counsel, the prosecution and the Crime Squad to go into court. Security had to check everyone before they entered the court room, which, with all the journalists as well, took quite some time. Eventually I was left alone with one of the security women. We exchanged small talk, I carried on writing, and in between I tried to read a funny novel, nothing too heavy, just something frivolous and flippant. The security lady made a passing comment as she had seen us many times and had chatted briefly to Matt and me. 'Your husband seems a very nice man.'

'Yes, he is, and he's also very innocent!' As I said it, I felt immense hatred for the prosecution and the National Crime Squad – anyone in fact who was in cahoots with them. I sat thinking, and a journalist came out of the court room. We had seen him before as he had on occasions appeared at hearings. Obviously this was an interesting case for his newspaper, and I say newspaper as it wasn't your everyday rag of sensationalism, gutter writing and over the top head-lines. This was a well-written and widely-read Sunday paper and he appeared to be a serious journalist. He introduced himself and said he guessed I was Matt's wife. He told me he didn't think there would be much happening that day, as the Carters' counsel had thrown a spanner in the works. This had been timed perfectly as it had stopped ET in his tracks. His words had hardly had an airing for once!

'So I'm going back to my office. See you tomorrow.' As he said all this, everyone filed out.

Apparently Adrienne and Matthew Carter had found a bug hidden in the side of their recently bought settee. They'd called a meeting with Costas and Androula. Mr Carter's barrister, Max Ross, appeared to be a no-nonsense, straightforward northerner, who Jack Sandler said didn't have time for ET and often let his feelings be known. Max Ross had taken centre stage and had told the judge that the prosecution still hadn't disclosed all the audio material and that therefore the defence couldn't work with the small amount they had been given. The Crown Prosecution had it all at their fingertips, and if they weren't prepared to disclose it to the defence, there wouldn't be a fair trial for the defendants. As the judge hadn't sworn in the sixty or so jury members yet, there was a great deal to discuss and think about before a trial could take place. Therefore, everyone was told court was over for the day and would begin again at 9 a.m. the following morning, when Judge Benedict would have to make a decision.

You may be wondering why I said sixty jurors, when there are usually twelve at a trial. The reason for this was explained by Mr Sandler: because it was supposed to be such a high-profile trial, the prosecution estimated it could take six months or more to conclude the proceedings. For that length of time you had to have extra people waiting in the wings to take over, as not many companies were prepared for a member of staff to take a six-month jury assignment. It didn't sound right, though; if you kept changing the jury how could they possibly keep up with what was happening in the court? The case was so complex that the right foot was struggling to walk in time with the left as it was. Talk about a shambles!

Before we went for a coffee Matt had to go once more into a conference room with his team. After all, they had to justify their large fees to the legal aid board. Carol sat talking to me, and Laura before she switched her mobile on said in a voice for everyone to hear, 'There will definitely be a trial; I feel quite sure of it!'

I found this remark difficult to hear, especially with her being Helen's sister. Although she's been supportive of Matt, she reminded me of Geoff at that moment. He hadn't been able to be there that day, but I was hurt that the two of them seemed to regard the court as interesting, as though it presented an exciting escapism from their uneventful daily routine. I certainly didn't need to hear Matt's aunt say that, yet she repeated it on the phone to her son. I was glad Matt was in the conference room and I ignored her comments, carrying on talking to Carol. By the time we left the court all the cameramen had gone and it seemed quite peaceful once more.

On Tuesday just Matt and I went to court. Carol and Laura had no need to return, although Laura did offer to come again with us. We told her it wasn't necessary. We needn't have bothered getting up so early, driving across London at 7.30 to avoid the build-up of traffic, as once they had all gone into the court room the judge decided the bug was an issue and that without all the tapes the defence were all at a disadvantage. So the trial was delayed until September, and once again we were put on a back burner.

Matt came out of the court actually grinning, partly from relief as he still hoped his counsel would achieve his dismissal and partly because he found it quite ridiculous in the court with both prosecution and defence arguing, and the judge trying to bring order. Max Ross and ET were like fighting schoolboys. Anyway, it was back to the drawing board. Here we go again, I thought.

16

A week later, while Jack Sandler's practice was in the middle of moving offices, he called a meeting with Edward Miles. It was going to be informal this time, in a hotel near his new office, which was in the process of being painted and carpeted and was in no state for a high class solicitor to hold any sort of meeting in. I'd been shopping in town when Matt had phoned to tell me to meet him at the hotel and that we could go home together.

When I arrived with my various carrier bags, Edward Miles's face was a picture. I went over to politely say hello and tell them I was going to have a cup of tea and take the weight off my feet, when he looked at me with his beady eyes and whispered, 'You can't listen to our conversation. You must understand that if anyone saw us all talking together all hell would be let loose! Couldn't you go and do some more shopping?'

I looked at him coldly. 'I find your attitude and what you say quite ridiculous! Having asked around the legal circuit whether your actions are correct, I am told no, absolutely not! You should have already launched an application to dismiss Matt, and it's rubbish when you say you have to wait for a trial! If the way you act was the norm, why is it that Mr Carter's solicitor Costas has asked me on a number of occasions why I sit outside the court? So have both Mr and Mrs Carter's barristers, Max Ross and Oliver Rushden. Max Ross is a QC, as is Oliver Rushden, I believe, so they must be even more informed than you are!'

I said the above knowing full well that Edward Miles wasn't a QC and that it was a sore point with him.

'Anyway, Mr Miles, you probably have your reasons. But your logic is way off. Please don't worry, I only came to tell Matt I have finished shopping and am going to sit about a mile away from you on the other side of the hotel lounge, drinking peppermint tea and eating an extremely fattening piece of chocolate gateau. Am I allowed to do that? I haven't measured the distance from where I am sitting, but quite frankly unless I suddenly develop X-ray ears I won't be able to hear a bloody thing!'

What is his problem and why is he so worried about me sitting with them whilst they have an informal chat? The more I saw of him, the more I felt he wasn't on Matt's side.

Our lives had fallen into a very odd pattern: endless court hearings, legal meetings both in the solicitor's office and in the barrister's chambers, reading files, court procedures and documents that the Crown Prosecution had invented, and whenever possible going to Bournemouth at weekends and then back to court on the Monday. By now Matt could have driven to South London with his eyes closed, he knew the journey so well.

Matt was usually informed of court hearings a week before, so he could at least try to organize his working time around them. But in the middle of March a sudden hearing was called. Matt outwardly took it very calmly, but I noticed that inwardly he'd become a walking volcano. That he hadn't erupted yet only gave the legal bodies the false impression that he was a soft touch, and someone they could push around. Well, they were in for a huge shock one day, as it couldn't last. When the time was right for Matt all hell would be let loose.

Anyway, getting back to this impromptu hearing, because I wasn't allowed to go into the court, Matt told me he always sat with the other defendants in the public gallery. ET would drone on and on, and then the defence would respond. This was usually Max Ross as he was the leading barrister for the defence and Matthew Carter. Nine times out of ten it would be a sheer waste of tax payers' hard-earned money, so with the assurance from Jack Sandler that it was only going to be a very brief hearing that was to start at 2 p.m. we avoided having the early morning rush hour drive. We arrived at court 5 to be told that it was a simple matter to answer a few questions the Crown had raised. Matthew Carter's solicitor Costas came over to me, smiling very broadly. As he wasn't my husband's solicitor, I don't know why he felt he needed to reassure me. But he said, 'Claire, it shouldn't be longer than ten minutes, twenty the most. This is just the briefest of hearings, and I still don't understand why you have to sit outside the court. It doesn't make any sense!'

'Well, Costas, if you don't understand it, how on earth am I supposed to?'

For a very quick hearing it seemed strange that a full complement of both defence and prosecution teams had graced the court foyer. ET and his support unit, William Channing, Tom Burns and Naomi Grossman, all walked in laden with files, together with three of Clarke's men, Dick Warner, Bob Kershaw and Gary Porter. Even the incognito, mumbling, bumbling, insignificant prosecution solicitor had come along.

Ten minutes, twenty minutes, an hour, two hours; I couldn't understand what was happening. Suddenly, Costas came running out of the court room and, half concentrating on his mobile phone pressed to his ear, called to me, 'Sorry, I didn't realize it was going to be an arraignment today, so it's taking far longer than we all anticipated.'

Then an ashen-faced Jack Sandler came out and shouted commands at me. 'Claire! Don't ask any questions. Ring Carol, Paul and Laura as quickly as you can.'

'Carol and Mike are away in Bath for a few days.'

'Oh hell! Can you try a mobile for either of them?'

'I'll try, but what do you want me to say if I get through?'

'I'll speak to Carol when you reach her.'

Mike's phone rang and I was relieved when he answered quickly. I asked him how they were and then I put Jack on the phone, who explained to Carol that he was very sorry to trouble her when she was taking a break, but that he needed her to find a police station and re-pledge her oath, as none of the defence counsel had remembered it was arraignment day and all sureties should have been told to attend the court and swear their oath again in front of Judge Benedict.

I didn't understand what Jack was talking about, and when he rang off he explained that an arraignment is the time when all defendants have to go in the dock and plead guilty or not guilty to the charges brought against them. So it was vital Carol try and find a police station, which I thought was easier said than done, and quite an imposition when she was having a short holiday with her husband. But Jack was adamant and said that if she came up against a problem she should ring his mobile and he would then talk to the sergeant in charge.

I honestly couldn't take it in! What else could possibly go wrong in this case? Hopefully, if you have come this far in my book, your imagination will be working in overdrive by now. If you can picture barristers for the defence plus their solicitors all on their mobiles pacing up and down the court corridors you'll understand that the scene was very weird indeed.

I phoned Laura and Jack asked her to go to a local police station too. She agreed to go as soon as possible and to phone me if there were any difficulties. I gave Jack my phone in case a call came in from Carol or Laura and I used Jack's phone to call Paul. He was in a legal meeting at the time and couldn't do anything about it, which was understandable. He said he would go first thing the following morning. From what I could gather, the defence had made one almighty cock-up. All the defence teams had assumed it was a simple hearing and had been quite taken aback when the judge had told all the defendants to go into the dock for their pleas. And Matt and the co-defendants were still bloody waiting there! They had to stay in the dock until all the sureties had been sorted out. It was one drama after another!

Jack said he would go and speak to Edward Miles, who was in the court room with Rupert Dunne, to see if they could speak to the judge about Paul. Within a short while Jack came out looking a little more relaxed, as Judge Benedict had said Paul's surety for ten thousand could cease immediately. The amount for Matt now stood at ninety thousand pounds. I phoned Paul and told him he didn't have to put up surety anymore for Matt, and as usual he was very interested in Matt's unbelievable situation. We left it that he would catch up with me later in the evening.

Jack gave me back my phone. It immediately rang and Laura said that the police were ridiculous. First of all no one at the station had known what to do: they hadn't heard of a surety, and no one was able to swear an oath. Second, when they asked her where the case was and who the main defendant was, she told the sergeant, Matthew Carter, but he looked at her blankly and said he'd never heard of him! His colleague said the same, which proves our point exactly. If the local police station not far from where the Carter family live have never heard about him and his alleged activities, why would Matt? Laura then spoke to Jack and he spoke to the sergeant in question, who took instructions on the phone. Finally Laura's oath was completed.

'Oh well, Claire, we're nearly there. Just one more surety to go.'

I don't recall Jack saying 'Sorry, we made a huge mistake.' Costas called out to me, 'So sorry. None of us had realized this was going to happen.' But Matt's team didn't say a word!

I checked my watch and it was nearly 5 p.m. I remembered that the parking place under the arches closed at 6 p.m. Usually we weren't at the court after 4, so had not yet found ourselves in this predicament.

The Carters came out of the court room with both their teams. They were free to leave the building as the solicitors for both Adrienne and Matthew Carter had spoken to the sureties and were going to meet them with Mr and Mrs Carter at a police station. As long as the solicitors didn't let them out of their sight until after the oaths had been pledged, they would then be free to go. Jennifer Thornton's mother came to the court and within a few minutes emerged with her daughter. But poor Matt was stuck! The judge had apparently said that Matt could wait in the foyer but that he was not allowed to leave the court building. He came out and looked very weary. The first thing he said was, 'Jack, I need to go to the loo.'

Jack looked rather embarrassed as he answered, ' I have to come with you, I'm afraid.'

This has to be such an antiquated law. Did the solicitor think my husband was going to unroll the toilet paper and use it to escape out of the window? But without making a fuss Matt allowed Jack to escort him to the toilet.

Sam rang to see how things were. She had just finished a dance class in Covent Garden and I told her about her father.

'What station are you near, Mum?'

I told her and she said she would come to the court if I could wait outside to let her in, as the court was unofficially closed to the public at this late time in the afternoon.

'You give me Dad's car keys and I'll bring the car back to the court from the car park.'

Sam arrived just in time to get to the car park before it closed for the night. She even managed to park near the court on a meter, but when she came in with me and saw her father standing next to Jack Sandler outside Court 5 she was very upset, especially when it transpired that if Carol's surety couldn't be done in Bath that day Matt would be locked up in the cells for the night. Sam wasn't going to hear any of that nonsense and she said so in no uncertain terms.

'If you put my Dad in a bloody cell you'll have me with him as I will chain myself to him. How dare you make my father suffer? He is already going through hell as it is, and today's mammoth mess is no fault of his. It's down to you, Mr Sandler, and the sheer incompetence of the defence teams.'

We were all standing outside Court 5, looking like idiots whilst the cleaner tried to hoover and mop the floor, at the same time avoiding our feet. It appeared that most people, including the judge, had left the court and we were there waiting for my mobile to ring. Eventually poor Carol called me. She and Mike had spent God knows how long looking for a police station; when they had finally found one, they were met with blank looks as surety was unheard of. Even though Jack spoke to them, it didn't help at all, so it had been left that Jack would tell Carol what to say the following morning, and she would pledge the oath at a Bath court. It sounded so peculiar. Surely if you swore an oath in the first instance you wouldn't need to go through the same scenario time and time again? It seemed very unfair to Carol who was having her leisure time disturbed.

In the meantime what were we going to do about my husband? Jack Sandler looked at all three of us and immediately said he would put up the surety for Matt, as both Sam and I must have looked as though we wanted his blood. It must have taken all of two minutes for Jack to go into a small back office in the court, where thank heavens there were people still working. After the oath had been taken Matt was free, but with the understanding that he would have to return to the court in the morning and meet Jack Sandler there to confirm Carol's pledge. Although Sam and I were very angry with the incompetence of the defence, we thanked Jack, as without his help Matt would have definitely have had to spend the night behind bars. That didn't even bear thinking about!

Needless to say the air in our car was quite blue. The two women in Matt's life were more than angry, and we had completely forgotten to phone poor Helen. Thank goodness her sister had told her that there had been an added problem. Sam kindly drove us home as Matt looked very strained. He spoke to Paul that evening and I think Paul was concerned for him as it seemed all the defendants' solicitors were in the dark as no one realised the consequences and Matt was suffering the most! In America they would have lynched you for such unprofessional handling of a case, but we Brits carry on regardless.

The next morning Matt had to quickly change his appointments and for once I stayed at home to deal with the clients who needed to see him urgently. Matt drove back to the court to meet Jack and go into a court room, but this time with a different judge who wasn't up to date with the case. In front of Matt and a few people scattered in the public gallery, the judge told Jack Sandler off, big time, as Matt Davidson was a defendant and in this judge's eyes should have been caged in for the night until Carol had been able to secure her surety. Apparently the judge went on and on saying that Mr Sandler should not have trusted his client, that he didn't know him very well, and that if the defendant had run away Sandler would have been liable to pay Carol's amount, the court would have looked ridiculous, and, above all, it wasn't ethical. Whether any of the press were tipped off about the situation we were never told, and we never saw it in print, but at least another fiasco had been sorted out and Matt had climbed over another hurdle.

In June Mr Carter's counsel called a hearing to complain that they were not receiving the required support from the Crown Prosecution, surprise, surprise! A lack of audio tapes was high on the list of their arguments. When we arrived at the court I noticed Jennifer Thornton looking very well and extremely tanned. I am not an expert on tanning, but it didn't look as though it came from a bottle, and the colour was too natural for it to have been a sun bed. We were enjoying our usual summer in England – one fine day, six bad days – so it seemed strange. As we made small talk with everyone within the defence circle, I thought I would ask Adrienne Carter if I saw her in the ladies room. I didn't feel I could ask Jennifer Thornton where her wonderful tan came from; it might have sounded pushy and rude as I didn't know her very well.

The following morning I bumped into Adrienne. We had a polite conversation and she said Jennifer Thornton had been excused that day as her young daughter had a cold. I remarked how well I thought Jennifer looked, and Adrienne said, 'Yes, she's had a lovely holiday with her boyfriend in Goa.'

'Oh, that sounds very exotic and obviously it must have been a very expensive holiday with the colossal court costs on top.'

As we were talking we caught up with everyone waiting to go into Court 6, and we stopped our conversation immediately as the Crown Prosecution were standing nearby. I was left outside to think about how much money it must have cost Jennifer Thornton to go away for two weeks.

That evening Adrienne phoned me and said, 'We weren't able to finish our conversation and I didn't understand your comment about court costs with Jenny's holiday.'

I told her what Jack Sandler had said ages ago. 'He put us off immediately from taking a holiday abroad, even for a long weekend, because he said the court costs were enormous, in the range of five thousand pounds, which would have been on top of the holiday price. So we just go for weekends to visit friends in Bournemouth and occasionally we are allowed to go up north for a change of scenery. But Jack was absolutely adamant that we shouldn't contemplate trying to go abroad.'

Adrienne's reply is unprintable! So I shall write it in my own way just so that you can get the gist of what she said. To put it very bluntly, numbers one, two and three defendants had all been given the court's permission to book their holidays abroad as long as the court knew the dates they were travelling and where they were staying. Their passports were given to them just for the holiday, as long as they were returned to the court within a day or two of coming home. It was frankly a piece of cake and there were no costs at all, other than the actual holiday of course.

I felt sick! Jack Sandler was supposed to be defending my husband and pulling out all the stops, giving him one hundred per cent support, but instead Jack had made Matt and me believe this case to be even more sinister than it was!

Matt phoned Jack Sandler, who said he was simply protecting Matt's interests as the court could have charged an enormous fee, and as Matt Davidson wasn't in Matthew Carter's monetary bracket, he didn't want Matt to cough up what could have been an unnecessary expense. Though he didn't know for sure, it could have been very costly.

But it wasn't, was it? It didn't cost any defendant a single penny and Sandler was talking his usual drivel. It was a two fingers down the throat sickening load of old codswallop! Sandler was the sort of person I wanted to smack. I didn't of course, but I wanted to! I hadn't trusted Matt's team before, so this was the icing on the cake. But until my tolerant husband saw the light himself, and stopped making feeble excuses for Jack Sandler and Edward Miles, there was nothing I could do. It was so frustrating, because Matt seemed to be protecting people whose job should have been to protect him! And he couldn't see they were dragging him down to a prison sentence.

A quick hearing was scheduled a couple of days later. This

time the hearing was instigated by Matthew Carter's defence team and it did work out to be fairly quick. They came away with a result, even though the trial had once again been delayed, until January 2006! It was good, though, because the defence had taken quite drastic steps to go above the trial judge and bring a three-day hearing to the Royal Courts in The Strand, where three lords would decide whether the defence were correct in their argument that the Crown Prosecution hadn't provided them with sufficient audio tapes. This major High Court hearing was taking place in September instead of the trial.

17

In August we were allowed by the court to travel by Eurostar and just enjoy Brussels and Bruges for a few days. Getting Matt's passport wasn't at all difficult and there was no extra charge. Even as I write this I feel Jack Sandler got away very lightly. We should have reported him on the spot. We had a great time and Matt loved the freedom of having his passport back temporarily. We both felt relaxed for the first time since 2003.

When we returned, a heavy parcel had arrived for me by parcel post, with no letter attached. Inside the wrapping was a large file with a one-line note that read, 'Thought this would be of interest to you.'

Bloody hell, it was an unbelievable file! Whoever had sent it obviously felt that the case was one-sided. The information was incredible. It was written years before the case, and we'll call it a 'secret file' even though there were apparently copies of it flying around. The gist of it was that the powers that be were deleting hours and hours of audio tape, mainly because they had storage problems. Towards the end of the file, three lines summed it up as follows: 'The operation has greatly assisted our investigation and has provided valuable intelligence. It has not, however, provided the detailed intelligence we had anticipated, and it is unlikely that the intelligence would be conclusive in a court of law.'

Wow! I read that paragraph over and over again, and then at the back of the file found more brief notes. One of the paragraphs stated: 'We are taking a close look at Frank

Brookes, Carter's former accountant. Brookes was replaced as Carter's accountant this year by Matt Davidson. Nevertheless, Brookes does not appear to be completely out of the picture, because his services have been needed to fill out some back-dated Inland Revenue returns. Please report any contact from Brookes.'

So, yet again there was nothing written about Matt. Don't get me wrong, I'm not complaining because there is a lack of material written about my husband. I'm complaining because he shouldn't be involved in the situation in the first place! The entire file spoke volumes and showed a very dark side to the build-up of a criminal case. It was corrupt and frightening, and reading it made me unsure who the bad guys were supposed to be!

We showed the information to Jack, although we knew what his answer would be even before he opened his mouth. He was so predictable by then!

'I'm sorry, but whatever evidence you get, even dynamite information you think may help, will not make any difference. The Crime Squad are determined to get Matthew Carter.'

It was a horrific state of affairs and whoever the professional personnel were behind the scenes, it was becoming more sleazy and corrupt by the minute! Reading the blue file took me back to Manchester and the forensic criminologist's words, 'Of course, tapes can be doctored to suit the police and the Crown Prosecution.'

In September we spent three days at the Royal Courts and guess what? I was allowed to actually go into the room. ET was reading from a lengthy document and his prosecuting pals kept nodding their heads in agreement, similar to the toy nodding dogs you see at the back of car windows. They were huddled together in a group with their anonymous prosecuting solicitor, and they did everything but applaud their leader whenever ET said something they believed was a magic moment! But to be fair to the defence they appeared to be completely on the ball, as they kept knocking ET's comments on the head!

I was sitting with Matt in the public gallery behind the Carter family and Jennifer Thornton. The general public were coming into the gallery as though they were day-trippers on an exciting away day outing! Crisps, sandwiches and cartons of juice were passed around. They talked quite loudly, ate noisily and slurped their drinks. We were quite relieved when they decided they didn't understand a word ET was saying and eventually walked out, looking for a meatier case.

By day three the defence lawyers had all been given a turn to put across their point of view. Max Ross, Mark Ronson and Oliver Rushden spoke very well; Edward Miles hardly said anything at all, though. He didn't have to as Matt wasn't high up in their priority. But Max Ross explained that there was no continuity as the tapes had been given to the defence haphazardly, and they had therefore been unable to work professionally with half-disclosed evidence.

Thankfully the lords all agreed with the defence and they won a minor victory that gave the prosecution a headache. It wasn't on a par with an Olympic Gold, though; it merely showed the Crown Prosecution they couldn't have everything their own way! Matt and I had learnt very quickly over the last couple of years not to get too excited about the prospect of the case being dropped and us being left in peace. It didn't seem to work that way. So, when I saw Matthew Carter smiling and congratulating his team, it seemed a little premature to be celebrating. That could only happen if and when ET and the supporting cast had a huge flop and the curtain came down forever on their dismal performance. You can only be upbeat and in a buoyant frame of mind when you win your case!

I must admit it was a good feeling to see the prosecution come unstuck for once! But for Matt it was still the same upheaval: endless, meaningless hearings at the court; meetings at Jack Sandler's plush new office; very private discussions at Edwards Miles's chambers with Miles's new friend Geoff! Geoff kept singing Miles's praises to me and really getting on my nerves. He would say, 'Edward says Matt is trial ready and has been for quite a while, Claire! That means they have everything in order and when the trial begins Edward Miles will sort ET out. Matt should walk away with a good result!'

This time Matt butted in and promptly said, 'I have never been trial ready and I have continuously told Jack and Edward that it's quite ridiculous. Where am I trial ready? They may want me to believe I am because it makes their job far easier, but I will never be ready for a trial as I haven't done anything wrong!'

I silently gave my husband the thumbs up, as it meant he wasn't accepting everything thrown at him by Miles, Sandler and the voice of doom Geoff!

Matt had achieved a tiny glimmer of light as the court was being more lenient towards him. He was allowed to go to Bournemouth or to the north of England at weekends without asking for their permission. It had only taken more than two years for the Crown Court to become fed up with Jack Sandler's faxes all the time, and thankfully someone with common sense had said that enough was enough. Matt Davidson was not running away.

January 2006 was upon us too quickly. The trial was set to start the week of the 9th. There would be the same build-up as before for the first few days; then a swearing-in process of goodness knows how many jurors and then wham! It would begin. As I write this, the memory of it all makes me feel quite sick!

Matt and I had been allowed to go away for the New Year for four days to Rome and, every opportunity we had, we went to the Trevi Fountain and threw coins over our shoulders to make wishes and pray they would come true.

Once again Carol and Laura came with us to swear their

oaths. It was déjà vu, the same number 1 court room, the same scenario, screens outside, security sitting alongside the screen and the same room with the grinning faces belonging to the Crown Prosecution, especially ET and the equally awful National Crime Squad representative Martin Clarke and his stooges, who had apparently said that this time there was no going back. They felt Matthew Carter couldn't stall the proceedings any longer and that they were going to get him and the other defendants.

Adrienne Carter didn't look well that Monday, which I suppose was understandable. She told me her stomach was in knots and she spent most of the morning coming out of the court and going to the ladies room. I sat in my usual spot, keeping my mobile on silent but speaking to friends who were interested and worried on Matt's behalf. It was always helpful to speak to people who gave you positive thoughts, especially when I looked at the sneering bewigged crew who were hell-bent on making our lives a misery. I also tried to write my notes for this book, but my concentration level wasn't at its highest as I thought of Matt sitting in the confined space of the dock and ET spouting a load of lies about him!

Clarke, Kershaw, Porter and Warner kept coming out of the court room, going in to their allotted room and closing the door. I sat very close to their conniving den and I could see that I was the one fly in their ointment. Our mutual hatred showed on all of our faces.

By late morning Carol and Laura had come out of the public gallery. They said that with the screen across the middle of the court it was very hard to hear what was going on. They'd understood snippets, but the words were muffled. Laura expressed her negative thoughts again, this time not directly to me, but to her son as she walked up and down the corridor talking on her mobile and gesticulating with her arms. She emphasized, 'There will definitely be a trial!' Her comment didn't help my mood.

But when Matt came out with his team and all the others behind him, it appeared that Laura's belief was not as cut and dried as she'd hoped or assumed. Another controversy had taken place. Someone had given an interview to a well-known magazine regarding Matthew Carter, which the Carters' defence teams had got hold of. With a trial looming, nothing is allowed to go to print beforehand. It's called *sub judice*, and it basically means no public discussion before a trial starts as it could sway the jury's decision. So once again His Honour Judge Hugh Benedict was thrown another setback just before this major trial could begin! In a very weird and strange way I was beginning to feel a little sorry for the judge. He had retired to his chambers, probably surrounded by law books and with a migraine, as he tried to make a decision as to whether a trial would be fair or unfair at that moment with the magazine being sold to the public for all to read.

Tuesday and Wednesday Matt and I went to court, and both days were spent apparently arguing. The judge hadn't reached a decision yet and the prosecution room seemed more low-key and less hyperactive. The police and the prosecution looked bemused, gloomy and a little frustrated.

Matt came out of the court and said, 'It's a farce in there. The judge has now overruled the decision to delay the trial because of the magazine article. He said the trial is going ahead and he's going to decide a trial date tomorrow. But, as it's Thursday, I don't think it will happen until next Monday.'

My husband was bearing up very well under the circumstances, showing great tenacity. I know he secretly hoped and trusted that Linda would turn out to have been right. After all, up until now she had been absolutely correct. Fingers crossed she would be proven right once again!

Adrienne's senior and junior counsel had apparently been out for dinner together the night before, and had both become ill with some sort of food poisoning. Adrienne

Carter, who hadn't been eating dinner at the restaurant with the barristers, was looking poorly herself, so Jazmin was there with her parents to give them some much-needed support.

Geoff had joined us that day, too, as a friendly support for Matt, though he said he could only stay for a couple of hours as he had a hospital appointment in the afternoon. So once again everyone went into court except yours truly, and just before lunch they all came out again. Although the judge had reiterated that the magazine article wouldn't make any difference to a trial starting the following Monday 16th January, the fact that Adrienne Carter's major team weren't in court meant that a full discussion about the trial wasn't possible. The afternoon session would therefore last only about an hour.

Geoff went home after lunch, but before he left we took him for a coffee and a sandwich. He and I were definitely starting to travel down different paths: he was on the black, the very dark and extremely negative no route; and I was on the white, the bright and more than positive yes route. He kept shoving obstacles in my face but I wasn't in the mood for more bad news! Because Matt still had belief in Geoff, he had taken him on a number of occasions to Edward Miles's chambers. Munching his sandwich, Geoff kept saying how much he liked Eddie, that he thought he was competent and that he also thought Eddie liked him! However, Geoff did say that he couldn't take to Jack Sandler. He thought he was an absolute snob and didn't gel with him at all. It's funny how opinions can differ so much. Away from the court, the surroundings and Matt's team, I am usually a 'people person' and make friends easily. But these people I viewed very differently and I definitely didn't agree with Geoff: if I had to choose I preferred Jack Sandler. Of course, the only thing that really mattered was what either of them could do to help Matt!

Matt and I went back to the court. Once again I watched everyone go into court and thought how sad it was for Jazmin Carter. She walked into the court room with her parents, but they went into the dock and she was left sitting on her own in the public gallery.

It didn't take very long before they all came out again. The police and the prosecution were actually running into their private quarters, the Carters were leaving the court with their teams and Jazmin, friendly as ever, said goodbye to me.

Matt went into a conference room with Jack, Edward and junior counsel Rupert Dunne, who out of the three of them was the politest and most pleasant. The room was bang opposite to where I was sitting, and because it was going to be a very brief meeting, they kept the door open. It wasn't a secret discussion; just a couple of minutes of general chitchat about the case and the fact that Adrienne Carter's major representation hadn't shown up, which in itself was peculiar. Then one of the Crime Squad team, balding Dick Warner, rushed past me and the conference room and ran into the court room. At the same time, the number three prosecuting barrister, quietly spoken Tom Burns, went in to see Matt's counsel.

Although Burns wasn't theatrical in the same way as Elliott Taylor or his second William Channing, I was sure I could hear my name mentioned. No one said anything to me, so I asked Jack Sandler after Burns had returned to the prosecution room and Matt's conference had come to an end. Jack said it was some rubbish about a paper cup I was supposed to have taken from the court room.

'Oh really! When do I go into the court? I think the answer is never!'

'Don't worry about it, Claire. We'll sort it out tomorrow and Matt will explain it to you on your way home.'

The prosecution room door was open and ET rushed past us into court as Warner ran out. 'What terrible, horrific deed

176

am I supposed to have done, Matt? There seems to be pandemonium coming from their room. It's as though they are plotting an evil attack against me as well as you! Whatever I am being accused of, will it be the gallows tomorrow for Claire Davidson?'

'What? Another crazy, weird day in the life of a British justice court room Claire? I don't profess to understand the structure of how a criminal case deals its hand in this wonderful system of ours, but I have seen for myself the legals playing their ridiculous games in the court room, whilst an innocent person like me has to sit in the dock and quietly bear the aggravation, stress and whatever they want to throw at me as a defendant. Fairness doesn't come into this at all; it's downright one-sided! Also, can you actually believe both Adrienne's counsel are ill? They must think we are all gullible! It sounds like they stayed away on purpose. Maybe tomorrow we'll find out the reason for it, but I actually doubt it! There's so much double dealing; you don't have a clue as to what is going on half the time! Also, when Tom Burns came into the conference room, he said something about you taking a paper cup. We all looked at him as though he had gone mad, and Jack said he would sort it out tomorrow. Who knows what the prosecution are talking about?'

We didn't have to wait long before we arrived at the final scene of the latest Agatha Christie novel, *The Missing Paper Cup Mystery*. Adrienne Carter called me that evening; it had raced around the court like wildfire and should have been headline news the following morning! CLAIRE DAVIDSON HAS STOLEN A PAPER CUP FROM A SOUTH LONDON COURT ROOM. Adrienne said she had phoned to apologise to me and to explain.

As I wrote earlier, Jazmin Carter had been in the court that day, and had sat behind two of the Crime Squad, Gary Porter and Dick Warner. When Warner had finished his paper cup of water, he'd left it by the side of his seat as he left the court room, and an usher had seen Jazmin take the cup and put it in her bag. The reason she did this was because she thought she could have it analysed and that maybe it would tie up the bugs in their house with Warner and his police friends. Quite inventive really! But somehow Chinese whispers always got it wrong, and whether or not it was wishful thinking on the Crown Prosecution and National Crime Squad's behalf, I became the culprit – even though I am never allowed in the court room! What brilliant deduction and intelligence bordering on genius! Another outstanding performance!

From now on I will re-name the CPS as the 'Calamitous Pathetic System'. Together with the bumbling police they really do a very thorough, professional and skilled job! They obviously hoped it was me as they wanted an excuse to ban me from the court foyer. For some reason they didn't like me looking at ET and his sidekicks with disdain! Perhaps I should make amends and invite all of them to come over to our house for an English civilized cream tea in the garden? Now, wouldn't that sound like a lovely, friendly plan? We could all play trivial pursuit and pass the parcel!

Anyway, Jazmin had been told off by her parents even though she'd meant well. I thought it seemed bloody ludicrous, especially as the usher and Dick Warner had to write out their statements and obviously had to change the name Claire Davidson to Jazmin Carter. What a paltry, childish and insignificant issue completely blown out of proportion, or maybe not! Because if you look at this from a different angle, why would Dick Warner be so worried about a paper cup? Perhaps they all had much to hide and the sheer fact that Jazmin had been shrewd and was probably on to them was really rattling their chains?

The following day when I saw Jack Sandler in the court canteen first thing in the morning, I told him I knew what had happened. He looked a little uncomfortable when I said, 'Where's my apology from the grotty police? And the usher must be some small-minded piece of work if she or he keeps an eye on paper cups being taken! They've made a huge song and dance over nothing! It sounds just like this entire case actually!'

So I sat in my usual place that Friday morning and stared at all the Crime Squad and the prosecution as they came out of their room with egg on their faces. The continuing saga of Warner's cup meant that he'd written a ridiculous statement that seemed to go on forever. He had finished the water, placed the cup by his side, forgotten to throw it away, etc. I thought, what a shame it was for Martin Clarke and ET that the assumed culprit, Claire Davidson, was as innocent as her husband and that Jazmin, who had simply been protecting her parents' rights to privacy, had seized the moment to get what she hoped was evidence. It sounded disgraceful to me – actually they had to have very warped minds. So I quietly applauded Jazmin: even though it had backfired for her, it had really and truly backfired for the Crime Squad.

I forgot to say that the date was Friday 13th January. Whether you are superstitious or not, Friday 13th can be a great day or a terrible day, somehow I couldn't imagine anything to do with this case being great! Geoff wasn't meeting us that day, so he knew nothing about the paper cup incident.

Looking at Adrienne Carter going into court that morning she seemed to me to look quite ill, but I seriously doubt if anyone else had noticed! At lunchtime everyone came out together. Matt told me the judge had said that the trial would start without fail first thing Monday 16th, after he had seen the jury. It meant that everyone had to be there at 9 a.m. sharp!

We were given more than an hour for lunch before the inevitable court room arguments began again. We had to have lunch with a member of Matt's team, so Jack Sandler joined us. It was the same antiquated idea as before, when

Matt wasn't allowed to go to the toilet alone or leave the building on arraignment day, so you can imagine how much more intense the situation was close to trial start. Matt required a posse of law enforcers just to accompany him to the loo, and to go to a pub or a café for lunch was unheard of without a solicitor or barrister with him. Jack Sandler had pulled the short straw and was escorting both of us to a pub.

I suppose having lunch in a bar with Jack was a good idea for Matt, as they talked about the football league and who was going to win the title and the cup, who was going to come up from the Championship and who would go down from the Premiership. As long as Matt wasn't going down that was all I cared about, but it did take his mind off the court and the amount of wasted time and money that had been spent on the case.

We walked back to the court and saw Jennifer Thornton coming out of a newsagent's. The cameramen looked at us, wondering if we were somebody! Nobody! Were we connected in anyway to the Carter case or just public gallery visitors? How I wished we were the latter, and just interested bystanders visiting English law courts!

Before the afternoon kick-off, Matt, Jack, Edward and Rupert were all in a side conference room, this time with the door firmly shut. ET was having a major argument with Max Ross. Neither of them gave a thought to court code of privacy practice, and as I sat there writing I couldn't help listening because they were so loud! Even the security woman sitting near me looked uncomfortable; she tried not to notice but it was impossible! You would have to be completely deaf not to hear their raised voices. They were in the conference room opposite me with the door wide open. ET told Ross to calm down, and Ross answered that he wanted the case wrapped up as he had another trial that was due to begin soon and this case was getting out of hand.

By now I was really concentrating on their interesting

words. Why would Matthew Carter's barrister want to move on to another case? Surely if there was going to be a lengthy trial starting the following Monday, Max Ross being the number one defence barrister would be prepared for it to take a number of months? It was very strange!

Matt finished his conference with his team and went with them to the security woman and into the court. Apparently they were the only ones there, and then a few minutes later ET, Max Ross, Oliver Rushden and Mark Ronson formed a queue at the security table and went into the court room. Matthew and Adrienne Carter, their solicitors Costas and Androula, and Jennifer Thornton and her solicitor Sean West were nowhere to be seen! Maybe they were allowed a longer lunch?

It was all very odd! I know I am beginning to sound like Jane Marple, but if you are reading Matt's story, you must be able to see that this case was far from straightforward! It was as though a mischievous being had descended upon us and somehow caused havoc all round!

By the time senior counsel for the other defendants came out of the court room and ET had gone into the prosecution room, which for once was very quiet, it appeared the opposition had all been sitting waiting for him. Matt, Jack and Edward went into the same conference room near me where Max Ross and ET had earlier had their pistols-at-dawn slanging match. Edward Miles looked quite ill and his face was deathly white. Jack called out to me, 'Matt will explain it all to you later.'

I answered, 'I thought there was something going on because before they went into court I heard an argument between ET and Max Ross.'

Edward seemed interested in this and said, 'Can you tell us what you heard?'

I explained every word I had written down and Edward Miles appeared to have been given a new lease of life. Jack suggested I list it all and anything else Matt and I thought could be vital. If it was possible to go to his office the following morning at about 11.30 he would see if it could be read out in court at the trial, which was definitely going ahead on the Monday coming.

As we walked out of the court to the car park, Matt explained what had occurred in the court room. 'It was very strange, Claire! As you know, I went into court with Jack, Edward and Rupert. I was expecting to go into the dock and for the court to be very busy, but we were the only four people in the court room. The other defence counsel and defendants hadn't arrived yet, and then all of a sudden ET came in with Max Ross, Oliver Rushden and Mark Ronson, in other words all the senior barristers. They formed a queue in the court with ET at the front. My barrister, Edward, was told by ET, "You are not needed for this particular private conversation that we are having with Judge Benedict in his chambers." Edward said, "I need to know what's going on, as it must affect me and my client." ET again said, "No, it's not necessary for you," and Edward was completely put out. He'd had his nose properly shoved out of joint. Jack piped up, "You can't go into chambers without Eddie." My team stood their ground. Edward may not be a QC, but he is still representing me and he needs to know what is happening.'

'Matt, I think Judge John Deed, Rumpole of the Bailey, and even Judge Judy herself would have enough script material for a winning television series here. I can't believe what happens in and out of the court room!'

'Claire, ET was going to broker a deal without my counsel's knowledge. Obviously I knew nothing about it, but together with the Carters' counsel and Jennifer Thornton's barrister Mark Ronson, ET was aiming to achieve a deal that would incorporate all the defendants and yours truly, but without the consent of my barrister. Apparently the deal he was brokering for me was going to be a soft option, whatever that means, and I could have then walked away. I told Edward what I thought of that! He said he hadn't accepted it anyway!'

'In the words of Geoff: "It's bloody outrageous." So after dinner let's go through everything we possibly can and give it to Jack. You never know, Matt, you may be the one calling the shots on Monday and causing a trial delay just for a change.'

We stayed up writing notes practically through the night. We listed one to about fifty points, and wrote down everything we could think of, including Matt's concerns that Edward Miles was being excluded from the elite QC circle. We took our list to Jack Sandler's office and Jack answered all the points in his usual around-the-houses fashion. We really didn't achieve anything other than getting everything out in the open! – I could see Edward Miles was suffering from low self esteem issues – 'well bugger that', the most important person suffering was my husband.

Matt managed to spend the rest of the weekend working on some of his client accounts. Bless him, he was quite amazing! I would never have been able to concentrate with a pending trial hanging over me!

Sunday night I couldn't sleep, so nothing new there. I thought of my parents and my father-in-law and hoped that my thoughts could be transferred into deep meaningful conversation wherever they were! I remember praying so hard to them and hoping they could hear me. I said, 'Please end this framed, fitted-up fiasco around your son and son-in-law. It has gone on far too long and is only benefiting financially the fat-cat lawyers with the ridiculous wigs and the Columbo-style grubby raincoat police.'

On Monday morning Matt appeared outwardly calm. He was sadly used to it all by then so seemed to take it in his stride. We played Sammy Davis Jnr, who else? As Matt drove steadily across London, the parking attendant could probably hear us coming. 'Mr Bojangles', 'The Candy Man' and 'I'm Not

Anyone' were being played at full blast and were brightening up the early morning bleakness.

At the court entrance there were no cameramen, very strange. Not because we wanted our picture to be taken, we certainly didn't! But they'd been there last week, why not now? The security guards at the front door acknowledged us in their usual friendly way, and the notice board told us it was still Court 1. When we got to the court there were no screens outside, no security personnel sitting at the desk and nobody waiting outside the court! Most peculiar!

'Let's go into the canteen and see who's there?'

The canteen was relatively quiet and Jack Sandler greeted us, 'Come and have a coffee and I'll tell you what's happened!' We looked at each other, wondering what was going on this time! Jack was speaking quietly on his mobile and when he'd finished he sighed and said, 'Judge Benedict has received a letter by fax from a surgeon at a North London Hospital explaining that Adrienne Carter was admitted into hospital just before midnight on Friday. The surgeon had to perform major surgery as she was in great danger of dying! Apparently she had yards of intestine removed from her stomach, so obviously the trial cannot happen now. Matthew Carter will be allowed to stay at his wife's side. When we go into court, which has been delayed for an hour, we'll know what the judge has decided.'

Matt and I were completely thrown off balance. This was something we'd just never expected!

'How sad! She did look ill last week and complained of stomach pains. That's stress for you! She puts on a good front, but she must have been really suffering.'

Now we understood why there were no cameras, no screens and no security.

I whispered to Matt as we walked downstairs from the canteen, 'I bet Judge Benedict has never had to deal with a case like this in his illustrious career! I know I prayed to my parents and your dad last night for help, but this is taking it to the extreme!'

The court session didn't take very long. Matt said that he felt ET's attitude had left a sour, bitter taste in the mouth. The man hadn't believed that Adrienne Carter was really ill! 'He actually implied that the surgeon's letter could have been fixed! Judge Benedict seemed to be the only compassionate person in the court. The rest, including the defence, looked very put out and offhand about Adrienne Carter's illness. Then ET suggested sending in a surgeon of his own choosing to verify the seriousness of her condition, but the judge immediately dismissed the idea. So basically Matthew Carter has compassionate time to be with his wife and a decision regarding a trial cannot be made at the moment.'

The police and the Crown Prosecution went into their room with deadpan faces. Their days of glory in the court room had once again been thwarted. Jack and Edward said they wanted my help and that, although it was a huge favour to ask, they believed it was necessary. The very fact that ET and his cronies had doubted Adrienne Carter's illness and the surgeon's statement had caused different opinions through-out the court room. His Honour Judge Hugh Benedict had disagreed with the prosecution, but all the defence lawyers had been left sitting on the fence as none of them knew what had really happened. So, it seemed that as I had been Adrienne Carter's friend and we had liked each other they wanted me to buy her a card and a small gift and go to the hospital to see if I could see her. If I then let Jack know, it would give him and Edward the upper hand over ET and everyone would understand the situation better.

I said I had planned to send a card anyway, but that, if Matt's team felt it was all right for me to do so, then I would go to the hospital in a couple of days. There was going to be a hearing regarding an update on Adrienne's progress in a week's time, so it would be a great help to all concerned.

18

I wasn't at all sure if I was doing the right thing, as my level of trust during this case had lessened considerably. I did know, however, having seen Adrienne Carter act on stage, that she was a bloody good actress! Whenever she'd come to the court she must have been giving an Oscar winning performance every time, because no one knew her true feelings. Yet both Matt and I did believe she must have been very ill, because I'd seen it in her face. The stomach pains she'd been struggling with had led to this almighty health hazard.

Matt was amazed that no one in the court other than the judge had offered any words of sympathy for her, including her own defence team. They never said anything at all!

There was no need to hang around the Crown Court, so we went home and I phoned Linda from my mobile as we drove. She reiterated the surgeon's words. 'She's very ill, this lady, at the moment, but she will get better. And Matt will not have to face a trial, I am sure of it. So tell him to concentrate on his work, Claire, and try to stop worrying. He is innocent and it will eventually be all right.'

Helen was very surprised to see us mid-morning. She had been waiting by the phone thinking that the trial had started. We explained about Adrienne in hospital and Helen was as shocked as we had been. I told her that Matt's team wanted me to go to the hospital because ET didn't believe the Carters and wanted to send a surgeon to give the prosecution his expert opinion on whether a fast one had been pulled. So it had been suggested by Jack Sandler and Edward Miles that I go to the hospital to put ET's doubts to rest. Obviously the defence would also have scored one over the Crown Prosecution.

It was arranged that I would go to the hospital on the Wednesday and Helen very kindly offered to take me. She wouldn't come into the hospital with me, though; she preferred to wait in her car. I'd already telephoned Jazmin to find out first-hand about her mother's health, and whether it would be an intrusion if I went to the hospital to see her just for a minute. Jazmin said her mum was very lucky to be alive as it had been touch and go on Friday night, but that if I just popped in for a minute she didn't think her mum would mind. She said her dad was by her mum's bedside most of the time and he looked very tired, but didn't want to leave her at the moment. After she told me the name of the ward I rang off.

I bought a get well card and a small gift and on Wednesday afternoon I went to the hospital feeling a little bit wary, especially as I realized I was being followed. It wasn't simply my imagination. I was really surprised when I arrived at Adrienne's ward. I don't know why but I had expected to find police waiting outside, and there weren't any! I asked at the nurses station if I should leave the card and gift with them, so I wouldn't disturb Mrs Carter, but they said that as long as I didn't stay long I could see her for a minute.

I wasn't prepared for the sight I was met with! Adrienne had wires and tubes practically growing out of her body and she was hooked up to blood, glucose, monitors and goodness knows what else! Matthew Carter was holding a small sick bowl, as throwing up was on the agenda and he was getting prepared. She looked very frail and I must have looked visibly shocked. I felt so many mixed emotions it's very hard to describe them, and I felt sad as I remembered she had visited me a number of times in the past when I had

187

been very ill and now she was the one in a hospital bed. Life is very weird; strange situations can happen in the blink of an eye.

I stayed just for two minutes. Adrienne was too ill to barely acknowledge my presence but Matthew Carter was very polite as usual and thanked me very much for coming. He apologised because he obviously wouldn't be able to come to the court, so inevitably there would be a delay, this time owing to his wife's desperately ill health.

I made my way down the stairs to the front entrance and bumped into Jazmin, who was on her way in to see her mother. We had a quick chat, but we both realized that the dodgy, rather sinister-looking man walking up and down the corridor was definitely there for a reason. It made me feel very uncomfortable and I couldn't wait to get out of the hospital. When I told Helen she was very cross with Jack Sandler for putting me in such a situation.

Matt was as sympathetic as I was when I explained about the hospital visit. I dutifully phoned Jack Sandler and repeated all that I had seen that afternoon. I could tell by the tone of his voice that he wasn't all that happy; as I was confirming that the surgeon's letter sent to Judge Benedict was one hundred per cent correct. Mrs Carter was very fortunate to be alive, but because she was so weak her husband would be excused from the court and a trial date would hang in the air until further notice.

I don't know what Sandler had expected me to say! I thought I was helping Matt's defence team by showing ET and the prosecution that Edward Miles had ways of finding out about the Carters in a totally above-board fashion. Maybe I had assumed that was the reason, but it didn't seem that way. I suppose, as the case was dragging on and on, the legal bodies were beginning to question whether there would ever be a door closing on this case. We were now in 2006, and the door was still very wide open! There were no answers at that moment and with both Mr and Mrs Carter out of action there wouldn't be for some time to come.

What a shame for these poor lawyers to suffer so! My heart bled for them! I realized how difficult it must have been for all of them to deal with such a disruption to their lives, travelling to the south London court week in, week out, dealing with the constant demands the case brought upon all of them. It must have been very arduous! It really doesn't bear thinking about, does it? So imagine how relieved I feel to know that these poor souls earn enough money to justify a Sunday lunch in the south of France, a summer holiday in the Caribbean, and if there is a week or two to spare over the Christmas period, skiing in Switzerland. What a terrible life!

I'm bloody sure I know whose shoes Matt would rather walk in!

Towards the end of January the court called a hearing regarding a progress report on Adrienne Carter's health. It was in Court 6, so there were no more security screens, and for the moment no more escort tours to the loo or to the pub for Dangerous Davidson.

I was lost in thought sitting on my own outside, but for once the hearing didn't take very long. Jennifer Thornton left very quickly and Matt had disappeared with his team to a vacant conference room. It seemed as though Matt's team always needed to have after-court conferences, maybe because their time and monies had to be stretched further. A quick hearing lasting for about an hour wasn't as lucrative as a full day's court session, so although Matt was the fourth defendant and his team were playing a minor part to the rest of the barristers and solicitors, they always made it seem as though these talks were very vital.

Looking along the corridor I heard ET laughing and I turned and saw him with his arms thrown very casually around Costas and Androula, solicitors to Mr and Mrs Carter. They all noticed me watching them and Costas whispered to

Androula to come over to me, which she did almost immediately. She had never spoken to me before that day, other than to politely smile, so the fact that it was necessary for her to waffle her way through a load of rubbish I found very amusing!

'Mrs Davidson, the next hearing has been changed from a morning session to the afternoon in three weeks' time.'

I stared at her without smiling and simply said, 'I already know.' I dismissed her remark and carried on writing as it was so obvious she had been sent over to me to cover their tracks. I knew then that they were all in it together, and that they knew I was the wrong person to have seen their display of affectionate togetherness.

Androula walked away looking uncomfortable. I wondered if the Carters had any idea who was on whose side. The mind games being played were now bordering on the ridiculous!

After the Greek lovey-dovey episode it was clearer than ever that as far as the case was concerned, you couldn't trust anyone! It was each man or woman for him or herself and, no matter whose toes were trodden on, the Crime Squad's main objective was to get Carter! Wasn't that a film title with Michael Caine?

The day before Valentine's Day, 13th February, my second mobile phone rang. I say second phone because it was an old one of Sam's after she had upgraded. The only person who had that number was Adrienne Carter. But I wasn't prepared for such a small, quiet voice. As a personality Adrienne was usually a force to be reckoned with – even her handshake was extremely powerful – but the woman at the end of the phone sounded like a small child.

She explained that she had come out of hospital at the weekend and was resting at home. Her specialist had told her how lucky she was to be alive and that she must take things very slowly as the healing process would take quite some time. She asked if it would be possible to meet me the following day. It was very important for my husband to know what was happening and she wanted to tell me face to face. She suggested a small teashop in Hertfordshire and we agreed a time. As she was about to ring off, a very high pitched piercing noise came through the receiver and she quickly said, 'Oh, I don't like the sound of this. Goodbye.'

I was left holding my mobile phone and both Matt and Helen looked at me enquiringly. The conversation must have sounded very odd to them, let alone the abrupt ending. As I was telling them about Adrienne's call, my mobile started bleeping in a Morse code type sound. This carried on for almost an hour. I didn't pick it up or listen to it; we just let it carry on bleep, bleep, bleep, bleep ... As I write this I realize how crazy it must seem and, believe me, it was. When this case began to unfold at the end of April 2003, we had no idea what madness was in front of us. By 2006 it was an out of control farce. You had to have a sense of humour and see the silly side of it all, because the dramatic side had completely misfired. By that point there were so many mistakes being made it could be renamed 'Operation Bungle-Botch'.

After my mobile eventually stopped bleeping, I checked my messages and saw I had twenty-two!

'Matt! Something very strange is happening! Can you believe I have so many voice messages? This must have something to do with Adrienne's call to me and why she rang off so quickly.'

Helen looked very worried as she listened to what I was saying.

'I know I'm no technical expert but with all the strange noises that have come through my phone I don't think it's the usual recording mechanism that you have on a mobile. I'll play it back and see.'

In theory I was right. Matt, Helen and I sat at the dining room table waiting to hear voice messages but there weren't

191

any, at least not meant for me. To explain it in an easy way, a bugging device had been put in place to tape Adrienne Carter's telephone conversations. When she rang my mobile, the 'intelligence' personnel made the almighty bloomer of connecting their state-of-the-art technology to my phone and bugged my mobile by mistake instead of hers! When I played the many messages back we heard voices belonging to three people who were in deep conversation together. One of the male voices I recognized was very much involved in the Carter case.

It was quite a jaw-dropping experience, I can tell you. We were sure the people chatting away had more than likely withheld their number, but it didn't hurt to check. So imagine my surprise when a mobile phone number was left on my phone. Matt rushed out to see a client and I said to Helen, 'I'm going to try the number but I bet it's switched off.'

Surprise again! The number rang. I couldn't believe it! A woman with a very posh voice answered the phone and I had to think quickly as I didn't have any lines prepared. I spoke with a very broad American accent, 'Gee, I'm sorry, I think I may have misrouted my call. Can you tell me who you are?'

Bingo! This woman was a very friendly, chatty lady who was only too keen to talk to someone from across the pond. She said I had called the largest law firm in Europe at their head office in London. They were called Ludovic Lyall. This information really caught my attention and I hoped I could carry on speaking in my new laid-back New York accent.

'Excuse the stupid question, but if you are a very large law firm, don't you have a switchboard with landlines? I can't understand why I have gotten through to a mobile number for one heck of a legal office! In New York where I come from, when you ring a company you call the main number, which is a landline.'

Again the lovely lady was extremely helpful. 'Let me

explain. Of course we have landlines, plus many switchboard operators and enough receptionists to meet and greet our clients, but we also have our own message centre where everyone uses mobile phones. Many of these phones are loaned out to lawyers, solicitors and the police to assist them where necessary with their ongoing enquiries. You have obviously dialled a mobile number and perhaps missed a digit, so lucky you, the number you've called is being used at the moment, and is in the middle of a major criminal case. Now what are the chances of that happening?'

'Oh, I would think practically never! So thank you so much for being friendly and informative. I really appreciate it, and you have given me an insight into the English high-powered legal system which is alien to me. Thank you once again. Goodbye.'

Helen laughed when I replaced the phone. 'You were so natural, Claire. If I didn't know you, I would have thought you were American. So what are you going to do now?'

'First I'm going to ring the Law Society, and then Jack Sandler to set up a meeting.'

I had to explain the phone incident cryptically to the Society but straight away the man speaking to me said, 'It is completely illegal for a well-known establishment of Ludovic Lyall's stature to tap a non-defendant's phone. I suggest you go to the top and speak to the chairman's PA. Tell her your complaint and she will know the correct person to deal with this as soon as possible, if they want to keep their very good name. At the same time, if I were you I would call my mobile server so they are aware of the situation. My goodness, the Sunday newspapers would have a field day if they ever got hold of this story. Good luck.'

I thanked him for his help. It was a relief to hear the Law Society speak completely in my favour, and even though I didn't rate my chances very highly for actually getting anywhere with this in the long run, at least I was going to give them all a bloody good fright and make sure enough people in the know would hear about it.

I called Jack Sandler and caught him quite unawares without going through the usual courteous channels. 'Hi, it's Claire. Have you heard of a law firm called Ludovic Lyall?'

'Of course I have. They are very famous as they are the largest. There isn't a lawyer out there who hasn't heard of them. Why do you ask?'

'Because I'm not a lawyer and I have never heard of them!'

'I can appreciate that, Claire, but I'm just a bit intrigued by the question!'

'Without going into a lengthy conversation on my landline, Jack, my mobile phone has been bugged and I would like to come to your office with Matt and have a meeting. I will then explain it in detail.'

'I'll call Edward and ring you back, Claire.'

Five minutes later Jack called to say that Edward Miles would see me at 3 p.m. on Wednesday. 'Will that be all right for you, Claire?'

'What? I'm going to be allowed to actually enter a barrister's chambers? Well, that's a first! Tell him it's fine, Jack, we'll be there.'

'Claire, aren't you going to elaborate so we have an idea what this is all about?'

'No, I think it will be better if I tell you both at the same time. See you on Wednesday, Jack.'

'Well, Helen, I must have worried them, I'm actually going into the chambers!'

'Good! They must be worried, Claire, if they have agreed to see you quickly even though they don't really know what it's about. They obviously realize something isn't right!'

The next one on my list was the mobile company. The automated answer service told me to press so many different numbers and endless options that I felt I would need to go to university just to comprehend what they were saying! Finally an actual person answered the phone, someone whose knowledge of phone technology had to be one hundred per cent better than mine and Matt's put together! I had to explain in a roundabout way the problem, as I wasn't about to tell the phone company about the Carter case. They were very positive when I outlined it as best as I could, and said they would send me a form to complete. If I needed their help further, just in case there was a court hearing and I wanted to prosecute the individuals who had tapped my phone, a member of their server team would be an expert witness, but I would need to play them the mobile recordings and obviously pay them for their time. I thanked him and said I would get back to them once I had seen a solicitor.

I decided I would phone Ludovic Lyall after the meeting with Matt's team. By this point Matt and I were wondering whatever was going to happen next!

On Valentine's Day, 14th February, I met Adrienne for coffee. She didn't look any better than when I'd seen her in the hospital. She walked very slowly, her skin was pale and she said, 'Look at my scar, Claire.' I nearly died! It was horrible! Any fool could see her stomach had undergone major, major surgery!

We found a table at the back of the tea shop and she spoke very quietly. Mr and Mrs Carter had in theory new representation again. Adrienne felt it was the right thing to let Matt know, as it wasn't really fair to him otherwise, as if the new counsel was accepted it would mean that a trial wouldn't happen until early 2007.

Explaining their decision to change she said, 'All our teams have started out all right and then they've fallen by the wayside. They don't really do very much to help us, and I think with me being so ill, we need people who are really going to work with us and gain points over the prosecution, because, let's face it, the others haven't done that! I know it's a hassle and we're sorry to put you both in this position, but as you can see for yourself I'm too ill to come to court for quite a few months anyway, so a new team will have the chance to at least work with my Matt, and I have a new lady solicitor, Frances Reece. She's really nice, Claire, and she actually listens to what I have to say!'

I didn't want to remind her that she had liked and trusted the previous teams as well! She looked too ill for home truths and I didn't want to be the one to put a spoke in the wheel.

She carried on in full flow. 'Claire, hand on heart, my Matt's an innocent person; he has been for years and years. It's just the name Carter and what it seems to represent to the Crime Squad. We are both very sorry you are involved in this rubbish; it should never have happened. And what is Sandler doing about it and the whispering Edward Miles? Whenever he speaks in court, which isn't very often, we can never hear him! They should be doing a lot more to try and get your Matt out of this. It doesn't make any sense, but I suppose it's all down to money!'

'I think you've hit the nail on the head, Adrienne. Do you remember when you rang off yesterday and there was a strange sound on our phones? Well, listen to this!'

I played the conversations back to her.

'Bloody hell! They must be talking about us! What are you doing about it?'

'We're seeing Sandler and Miles tomorrow at the chambers, and we'll see what wondrous ideas they come up with. We'll take it from there!'

'If they don't know about our change of legal teams then tell them, because there's a hearing this coming Friday afternoon. I'm not sure of the time but they can find out for themselves and let you know.'

I wished her well and told her to go home and rest. I went home with all sorts of thoughts floating around in my mind. Matt reacted as I thought he would, with compassion, which was typical of my husband. He just said, 'We'll see what happens in court.'

Going into Edward Miles's chambers the next day felt peculiar. Both Jack Sandler and Edward Miles looked a bit twitchy. I explained about Adrienne's telephone call and our subsequent meeting yesterday and all it entailed.

Miles's reaction was sheer horror. 'Impossible! They can't change teams again! The judge won't hear of it, I'm sure!'

'I think with Adrienne Carter being so ill, Judge Benedict may agree a change. We'll have to wait and see. I've brought along my mobile.'

Without a single hesitation Jack said, 'Well, that smacks of Elliott Taylor!'

He didn't know we called him ET for short. I looked at Matt as Jack had said exactly what we wanted to hear. We nodded back at Jack. 'Yes, we agree with you.'

'Right, I think I'll have this investigated. We'll have to see where this was done in the first place!'

Miles interrupted him, 'First of all we need to find out if there is definitely a hearing this week. I'll check with the court now, because we officially know nothing about Carter changing from Max Ross to whoever he's chosen this time.'

We watched him as he dialled. He definitely didn't look happy, but why would we worry about that? We hadn't been happy since the beginning of the case! It took seconds for the court to confirm that the information I had passed across to him was correct and that there would be a hearing this coming Friday at 2 p.m. They had just been about to fax him and Jack to let them know.

'Absolutely ridiculous! Carter cannot get anywhere with this! But as we will be meeting at court in two days, I think we should bide our time. We'll make a few quiet enquiries and see what transpires, and the day of the hearing we'll meet in the canteen at 1 p.m. That will give us an hour to talk things through.'

I watched Jack as good old Eddie had completely taken over and really dismissed his idea of ET very quickly.

'I will remind you, I do know whose phone it is! It's the message centre at Ludovic Lyall's! What we need to find out is who is actually using the phone now. In other words, who has borrowed it?'

Jack blinked at me and mumbled, 'Oh yes, I forgot,' and Edward butted in quickly, 'Leave it to us, Claire. We'll definitely let you know when we see you on Friday.'

We left soon after and I didn't feel at all confident that for some reason Edward wouldn't allow Jack to do anything at all! I hoped my thinking was wrong!

We met Sam in town after our meeting and played the recordings to her. Our daughter's thoughts on this latest cock-up were delivered with quite colourfully creative words quite beyond our comprehension. Sam explained to me in easy terms that the voice recordings on my particular phone would only be saved for one more day, so a technical whizz-kid she knew used his expertise and re-recorded it all on to another phone. That way it would stay safely away from our home and at a neutral address where it would be kept as evidence should we need it.

Matthew Carter's new team were going to be on show in the canteen just before the court hearing. Sitting with Jack and Edward, we waited for them to say, 'Guess what we've found out!' or 'We have some news for you'.

But not a word, no! Instead, they dived into a lengthy chat about Matthew's and Adrienne's new legal bodies. They didn't know Matthew Carter's new solicitor; he was an out-of-town man and they had never heard of him. But they knew who Frances was, as her office was just around the corner from Edward Miles's chambers. Both the new barristers were very well known to them, but they still couldn't see the judge agreeing to the change, Blah, blah, blah, blah; they droned on and on, obviously hoping we'd have forgotten about the insignificant subject of 'the bugging of Claire Davidson's phone'. I wasn't at all interested in who they knew and who they didn't, and I knew Matt wasn't either!

My patience and tolerance level were by this point zero, so I interrupted the Who's who? of legal royalty and asked, 'Aren't you going to tell us about your findings with regard to my bugged mobile phone, Jack?'

The other part of the double act, Edward, had exhausted the conversation and had disappeared into the robing room to put on his gown and wig. Jack stared at me. Even as I am writing this I still cannot believe what he said.

'Claire! You know how very busy lawyers and solicitors are. We always rush around here, there and everywhere, getting taxis to and from court. I've left my mobile in a taxi before, and that is probably what's happened this time. Someone left a phone in a cab and, for some technical reason that only a phone company would understand, it misrouted to your mobile. I'm sure it's happened to others; we just don't hear about it.'

I fixed my sarcastic serious stare that I knew he couldn't deal with. 'Once again, Jack, you seem to have forgotten, though not very convincingly. However, I will give you the benefit of the doubt and speak very slowly so you can understand me. Adrienne Carter rang me on a mobile phone to arrange to meet me the following day, to talk about their new representation. She rang off very quickly when a high-pitched noise intercepted her call, and immediately after I had rung off I received a load of Morse code style bleeps. Conversations were recorded directly on to my phone by mistake, and the number they had bugged my phone on was a mobile. After trying the number I found out from a very helpful lady that it belonged to Ludovic Lyall's message centre. It isn't rocket science, Jack! But don't worry about it! I'm not your client! Matt is! Let's face it, you haven't done anything for him, so why on earth should I think for a moment that you would help his wife, who isn't even a defendant? Just forget about it. I will deal with it myself.'

'Claire, I'll speak to an investigator next week for you.'

'No, don't bother!' I walked away, knowing categorically that the team were definitely not on my husband's side. If only Matt realized it!

Apparently the hearing went swimmingly for Matthew Carter, and a changeover was completed very quickly. It was as Matt said afterwards, 'A piece of cake.' Edward Miles's prediction as usual had been totally wrong. Anyway, Adrienne's ill health plus a new team with so many files to go through and audio to listen to meant that the trial had been pushed back to 6th February 2007. It was probably already documented as the longest-running prosecution case ever, and who knew if it would even go ahead then? I had visions of the Crime Squad and the CPS pulling their hair out! What a shame for them! Maybe this will be a case that will carry on until the end of time! A picture of Elliot Taylor and DCI Clarke came into my mind, no teeth and zimmer frames – still trying to win at 100 years old – and still failing.

19

I didn't wait for Jack to do anything regarding the phone. I rang up Ludovic Lyall, as the Law Society had suggested, and told them that my mobile phone had become intertwined with one of theirs. Almost immediately I was given an appointment to see someone the following day. So, with my mother-in-law accompanying me, I travelled to Docklands and went into the largest reception area I'd ever seen, at least in this country. I lost count of how many receptionists were sitting in line and how many plasma screens were dotted around. It was a town on its own. Helen and I were amazed by the size of the place and if we came across as bumbling bidders so much the better!

The man we saw was pleasant enough to begin with. I didn't go into details about the Carter case, but I bluffed my way through some waffle, telling him I knew someone who was going through a court case and that ever since this acquaintance had contacted me my phone had been connected to Ludovic Lyall's message centre. He said he thought that was very strange and quite unlikely, and that perhaps I had made a mistake. I told him about my conversation with the friendly lady and suggested he look up the number on his computer system.

'Yes, you're quite right. It is one of ours. Obviously I have no idea at the moment who has taken the phone on a loan basis, but I'll make some internal enquiries and see what I can find out. Give me a couple of days and I'll call you.'

Unfortunately, he had the same memory problem as Jack

and Edward. He didn't phone me and I wasn't convinced that he ever would, so after three days I rang him.

'Hello, Mr Phelps, it's Claire Davidson.' I practically heard him sigh. 'You said you would call me as soon as you had checked with your message centre?'

'Yes, I'm sorry, I've been extremely busy. Quite frankly, Mrs Davidson, the phone is out on loan but owing to data protection I cannot say who is using it.'

'Yes, I thought as much! Never mind, I'll deal with it myself.'

The entire process had started to feel like a self-service checkout queue. As no one was prepared to help us, it had turned into a do-it-yourself job! If I'd had magic powers I would have thrown a load of magic dust around, taken a law degree overnight, passed with flying colours and become a High Court judge in a week! However, that was never going to happen. Besides, I didn't need to study; all I needed was to apply common sense and logic, something this mob were all lacking! I realized that unless I was prepared to do it for myself, nothing would be done. I received the same treatment from Ludovic Lyall – what a coincidence! There was a bloody brick wall right in front of us: whenever we saw a glimmer of light someone dimmed it immediately. This was a movie, or at least it should have been.

The mobile phone situation actually became worse, if it's possible! Helen went once a week to a senior citizen local club, and she would spend a pleasant afternoon watching entertainment and having tea with people she'd known for a long time, including Laura and Leslie. She didn't use a mobile phone at all, so to this day I'll never fathom out what happened. After she had come home and we had finished our evening meal, my mobile phone began making the bleeping noise again. It wasn't for too long this time but, nevertheless, it was disconcerting. Playing it back we were amazed to hear my mother-in-law's conversation at the club. Somehow it had all been recorded on to my mobile. Well, what incredibly useful information for the police. Who did they think Helen was, Old Ma Baker? Could it be that she and her sprightly but somewhat elderly comrades were planning a heist somewhere? Strange isn't the right word for all of this! How about bloody incompetent, not to mention the huge amounts of public money they were wasting!

Helen was amazed when she heard her voice clearly on my phone. 'Well, I never! I feel as though they have planted a hidden microphone on me. Whatever next?'

We made a joke of it and said she should audition for the next *James Bond* film! But it really wasn't a joke. It had now become the weirdest case ever, and one I don't think even Hercule Poirot and Jane Marple working together could have solved very easily.

However, out of something bad often comes something good, and Matt had finally had enough and seen the light for himself.

Before the hearing when Matthew Carter introduced his and Adrienne's new teams for the judge and court's approval, Edward Miles had taken Matt aside and quietly told him, 'When the judge asks if we object to the new representation, I advise you very strongly not to say yes, because knowing who Matthew Carter is, you could find yourself and your family under concrete if you go against him. It's best to let it go and we'll carry on as we have before.'

This was a conflicting, contradictory load of old hogwash advice, as a few weeks ago Miles and Sandler had been all for me visiting Mrs Carter in hospital so they could come across as the good guys who seemed interested in Adrienne's health. What a huge mistake we made in choosing this team!

The only reason Matt took Edward Miles's advice wasn't because he believed in his very dramatic words, I don't think he did for one moment, but I think because Matt silently hoped that maybe this time Miles would come up trumps and show good judgement on the matter. However, in the court it went completely pear-shaped; as Edward Miles didn't stand up to object to Mr and Mrs Carter's proposed new legal teams, Judge Hugh Benedict made a point of directing his next comment to Matt.

'Mr Davidson, you appear to have no objection to Mr Carter's proposed change of counsel for the third time. Am I to understand from Mr Miles that you won't be asking for a dismissal for the time factor you have had to spend on this case, besides anything else?'

It was a blessing that I hadn't been allowed in the court room or I would have really let rip at Miles and ended up behind bars for contempt of court. It was worse considering that Edward Miles had repeatedly told the court, 'Matt Davidson is trial ready'. It wasn't true, of course. Matt Davidson had never been trial ready and both Jack Sandler and Edward Miles had known that from day one!

So now Matt was at long last ready to fight back. I remember Matt speaking sharply to Edward Miles on the phone. Miles tried to cover up his tracks but Matt wasn't interested and he decided to go the same route as Matthew Carter and change representation. But again Matt had a brick wall right up against his face. Unfortunately Judge Benedict disagreed and wouldn't let Matt leave Jack Sandler and Edward Miles. I know this first-hand because I was allowed into the court for that as it wasn't directly to do with the case.

The judge was adamant, 'Mr Davidson, you are in a totally different league to Mr Carter and I am surprised that you wish to change. It's been a very long case and people often go through a temporary fall-out with each other. I suggest you go away and talk it through together, because I will not allow you to change your representation.'

It sounded as though Miles and Sandler had a fan club within the court system. This Crown Court trial judge wasn't a bombastic character; he actually appeared quite personable, if a judge can be called that! But his steely determination in making Matt stay with representation he didn't want and even more importantly didn't trust was ridiculous and one hundred per cent unfair! Matt went to court three times for the sole purpose of trying to get through to Judge Benedict and hopefully make him realize he had to change his legal counsel. Even our solicitor friend Paul went to court and directed his legal terminology to the judge. But it made absolutely no difference at all to the judge. He was emphatic, 'You are not changing your team, Mr Davidson!'

Why was Matt being persecuted like this? The icing on the cake was that Miles and Sandler came to court whenever Matt called a hearing to change his team. They would then make sure that Matt wasn't able to leave them. How could they be so thick-skinned? I always thought freedom of choice is something we have in this country. If you are not happy with the service you are getting from an individual or a company, you must and should be able to walk away. No one with any self-respect clings on to a client who doesn't want to stay, but this ghastly twosome did just that!

Jack Sandler then apparently wrote to Judge Benedict informing him that Claire Davidson had shouted and upset him in front of his staff a year or so ago. What a wimp! So, just in case, Judge Hugh Benedict visualized me with knuckle dusters, ready to lash out at any given moment, I photo-copied relevant papers that gave me a good deal of credence from very influential people, and I offered to go on the stand to answer any questions His Honour wished to ask. That way he would see for himself that I wasn't a hooligan as Sandler had tried to portray. It couldn't have been further from the truth, and I wasn't going to let Jack Sandler get away with lies! He had got away with those for far too long, and my kind husband had been much too lenient.

By June Matt had become desperate and called another hearing. This time he said that, owing to complete and totally irreconcilable differences, he would rather represent himself than have Jack Sandler and Edward Miles. Finally, Judge Benedict had to agree, as it meant legal aid was no longer relevant. Sandler and Miles walked out of the court, this time defeated and very angry. They weren't prepared to work for nothing, but legal aid for a criminal case of this magnitude had meant big bucks for them. No wonder they'd held on to Matt for dear life!

I sat as usual outside Court 5, and was both amazed and relieved to see them marching past me with stony-faced expressions. This wasn't going to look very glowing in their list of achievements!

Jennifer Thornton came out of court and said, 'The judge has allowed you to come in, Claire.'

I never expected that and I sat in the public gallery behind two policemen from the National Crime Squad. I heard Judge Benedict say, 'Mr Davidson, as you have made the decision to represent yourself and you are a professional man, you will need all correspondence sent direct to you from the prosecution, which Mr Taylor will organize.'

Matt came out of court with his head buzzing! On one hand he was glad that Sandler and Miles were no longer contributing to his downfall, but on the other he thought about his accountancy work piling up just when he had taken on the massive task of representing himself!

If you think about it all logically, both Mr and Mrs Carter had QCs and solicitors. The same went for Jennifer Thornton, who was happy, if that's the right word, to stay with Mark Ronson and David Shaw throughout. They appeared to be level-headed and fairly responsible and she seemed to have confidence in them and the decisions they were making for her. But the fourth defendant in the list of Who's who? Mr Absolutely One-Hundred-Per-Cent Innocent had to represent himself. What an almighty headache!

Looking back at Edward Miles's and Jack Sandler's

handling of Matt's case, it was a joke, especially the famous line about Matt Davidson being 'trial ready'. They had not sought out a forensic accountant to come on board and report on Matt's work. They did say they had someone in mind but he never materialized. They were no loss at all.

Within a few days the CPS sent Matt a file from a tax inspector, Warren Erskine. This was a new file to Matt. It appeared that Mr Erskine had been appointed by God knows who throughout the middle 90s, and that he'd had his suspicions about Mr Carter's taxes long before Matt took over as accountant. Having read the file, Matt wondered why the tax office had never queried Matthew Carter's tax returns when Matt had filed them in 1998 and 1999. There was never a problem with them at all! Surely if there had been a major enquiry and continuous investigation into a client of Matt's, it would have been proper and correct for the tax office to make that known to the accountant in question? How can it be legal? Isn't it called entrapment?

Poor Matt was completely bogged down with court hearing papers, so my mobile phone was no longer a major issue. It seemed silly to pursue it as the conversations had now stopped and Matt's situation needed even more support than before. Geoff agreed to come to court as often as possible and Matt would calmly carry on as best as he could. These were very difficult times: the trial was only five months away.

At a hearing later in the month, Adrienne Carter attended, looking very much better. She accompanied her solicitor Frances Reece into a small conference room opposite the court room. Frances Reece came across as calm and collected, and her expression never changed. Although she was quietly polite to me on the surface, she wasn't going to give anything away, quite a dark horse! With Adrienne being the opposite, I wondered how their relationship worked.

Matthew Carter's solicitor Stuart Parry appeared to be very

different. He came and spoke to me and said very similar things to the previous solicitor Costas.

'Do you have to sit outside?'

'Yes, always! I'm a witness for Matt, unless of course there's a hearing that doesn't directly concern the case.'

'Well, Claire, my wife is also a solicitor and together we read the CPS evidence they have compiled against your husband. It's absolutely bizarre! He should have been dismissed years ago!'

'We know that, but he had a rubbish team.'

'Well, he's allowed a McKenzie Friend to help him in court before the trial and right through it as well.'

'I've never heard of a MacKenzie Friend. What does it mean?'

Stuart Parry spoke quietly to me in a corner of the court foyer just as ET walked past with his sidekick William Channing. Looking at their expressions you could see they were curious. Why was Matthew Carter's solicitor talking to me and what about?

'First of all, I'm not being pedantic, but it's McKenzie and not Mac! It's well-documented in all law libraries about a divorce case that was brought to court in 1971 by a couple called McKenzie. The husband represented himself with the help of a friend and together they won the case, which was the first of its kind. A McKenzie friend is now recognized in most courts. He or she is usually a non-legal person who will help you with your notes, but they cannot stand up in court and speak on your behalf. They are just in court as your confidante – someone you really trust who will support you throughout the trial.'

'Well, for Matt the entire case has been alien to him, and now he finds himself alone without any professional help. I suppose any kind of assistance would be appreciated. I'll tell him what you said, and thank you for the help.'

After lunch I told Matt that Stuart Parry had said it was

bizarre that he was still in this case. I also told him what Parry had advised. In earshot were Tom Burns and Naomi Pearlman, the third and fourth prosecuting barristers. Pearlman never cracked her face and it was strange to actually hear her speak.

'If you are a witness for your husband, Mrs Davidson, I don't think you can be a McKenzie Friend as well. I'm not sure though, so you had better find out, if you are considering both.'

'I haven't considered anything yet, but I will bear it in mind and find out. Thank you.'

Tom Burns seemed to agree with her and said the same thing.

'I'm not sure I want to be a McKenzie Friend. My husband shouldn't be in this situation in the first place!'

I turned my back on them as there was nothing else to add. Anyway, I didn't want to converse with them; they were the enemy trying to put my husband behind bars!

On the way home Matt and I talked about friends we could ask who would have the time to come to court on a daily basis. I suggested a very close friend Julia who had offered before to come to court if we needed support. Julia had been our friend for many years and has a very generous nature, mixed with kind-heartedness and a direct, straightforward manner. Still, Matt wanted to understand more about McKenzie Friends before he asked anyone. From the Internet we learnt that it would need someone to give up a lot of their time. Julia's prior commitments at home with her family meant that it wouldn't have been fair to have asked her. Then Geoff stepped in almost immediately, as though he'd been expecting Matt to ask him and was actually prepared for the question. Very odd!

Throughout October and November there were numerous hearings, and Matt was busy writing notes. I'd thought Geoff was supposed to be doing that, but instead I often saw Geoff in the foyer talking to Adrienne Carter's junior barrister or one of Matthew Carter's legal team. I couldn't quite put my finger on it, but something didn't seem right!

Helen, Sam and I were very proud of Matt. He gave all his clients his full attention and still managed to prepare himself mentally for a possible long trial where he was defending himself! The prosecution seemed to be a little worried about that prospect, because ET stood up in court and said they all thought Mr Davidson should have representation.

Judge Benedict didn't agree. He said, 'Mr Davidson is a professional and should be able to handle it.'

When Matt came out of court he wasn't his usual self. 'Does the judge think I'm an accountant and a learned lawyer as well? I don't know anything about legal jargon; I'll probably interrupt ET at times when I shouldn't and then I'll be in contempt of court!'

'That's what your good old McKenzie Friend Geoff is there for, Matt! I would love to help you in the court but they won't let me.'

'I wonder why, Claire!' Matt grinned. It was good to see him relax, just for a moment. I was very frightened for his health and his mental state. How was he coping with all this? It was a major criminal case, possibly lasting six months. What did Matt Davidson know about that? Nothing!

Going to a local County Court and challenging a parking fine was one thing, but this was in a totally different league altogether!

Early in December there was an informal hearing without defendants but because Matt was his own legal counsel ET came over to him in the court room and said, 'We need your McKenzie Friend's details.' He pointed this out to the judge, who acknowledged that he would ask Geoff for his name and address later. Matt looked at his friend, who had gone as white as a sheet.

'I'm not standing up giving my details!' He looked very shaky and Matt thought it was very weird. To be blunt, if

Geoff couldn't stand up and face a few defence and prosecuting barristers just to give his personal details so they had everything in place before the trial started, how was he going to be a wonderful support to Matt in a packed court with a jury, the press, police and the general public in the gallery? I began to worry!

Driving home, Matt said, 'Next week, Claire, the 13th December, which I think is a Wednesday, ET said I should join the prosecution and defence barristers at his chambers to go through some of the files with them. As it is coming up to the Christmas holidays and they are going to have a working lunch Geoff has been invited as well. I told him I had a tax meeting in the morning but could be there in the afternoon about 3 p.m. if that was all right. It's agreed I'll get there as soon as my meeting's over.'

Matt met Geoff at Chancery Lane station and they walked around the corner to ET's chambers. Helen had kindly baked a couple of apple strudels for them to take as it was coming up to Christmas. I thought she was barmy; there were far more deserving people around to bake cakes for! But Matt didn't seem to mind and if he wasn't fussed then it was fine with me! When he put the strudels on the table, Adrienne Carter's pompous barrister, Philip Underwood, laughingly made a very stupid comment. 'Are you bribing us, Mr Davidson?'

Matt said, 'No, my mother poisoned them!' They all laughed and, believe it or not, still ate them!

Matt and Geoff went into a very small room with Tom Burns. He was prosecuting barrister number three, so it seemed ET must have dished out the orders beforehand. Burns spent a couple of hours going over documents that the CPS had been working on that morning. This was to bring Matt up to date, and to help him understand as best as he could all the elements of the prosecution case. When they had finished reading and tea was over Tom Burns sat back in his chair, hands behind his head. Geoff and Matt sat next to each other. It was all very cosy, and Burns without any prompting said completely out of the blue, 'I would love to defend you, Mr Davidson. Of course, we all know you are completely innocent.'

Matt was both stunned and very surprised by this admission from the opposition. Saying a hurried goodbye, Matt and Geoff went for their usual coffee and think-tank discussions. Geoff wasn't his normal flamboyant, talkative self. In fact, Matt said he was quite the opposite! Matt quite rightly was very excited and upbeat about Tom Burns' open remarks.

'Geoff, what are your thoughts regarding Tom Burns and what he said?'

'What was that, Matt?'

'I mean when he said he would love to defend me and that they all know I am completely innocent.'

'I didn't hear it, Matt.'

'What? You were sitting next to me, Geoff, you must have heard it!'

'Afraid not, I was doodling and had switched off.'

'Switched off? We were sitting in a very small area and you are telling me you heard nothing?'

'Sorry, Matt, nothing at all!'

'In which case there is nothing more to say.' The conversation ended very abruptly and so did Matt and Geoff's friendship.

20

Matt walked to the station with mixed feelings. He telephoned me and repeated what Burns had said. I was ecstatic!

'Matt, that's fantastic! For a prosecuting barrister to say words like that it must mean you have a bloody good chance of walking away from this prolonged nightmare of sheer misery!'

'I'll explain it to you when I get home, Claire. I'm about to go into the underground so the mobile will go off in a minute.'

When Matt walked in I expected him to be all smiles, but he seemed subdued and miles away. He told me what happened at the meeting and what Geoff had said.

'He must have heard it, Matt! It doesn't make any sense! He's covering up! He's been got at! Or maybe he's been offered some money and it's a wind-up?'

'What do you mean, Claire'?

'I'm not sure really myself! But let's talk it through. ET knows you are a novice, at least as far as the law goes, and maybe he wants to get all four defendants tied up neatly in a package. You are the one fly in the ointment as you are representing yourself. The case against you isn't so much as flimsy, it's completely transparent, and the jury won't need to be rocket scientists to see that. Therefore as well as getting people to realize that you are definitely not guilty, you will also gain the sympathy vote. Even if the judge doesn't see it, the rest of the prosecution team do! So let us suppose that ET is aiming for deals all round.

'What if what ET wants from you is to gain some false security? He tells Tom Burns to say those things to you and good old Geoff is in the loop as well, so he plays along with the charade and pretends to switch off. Let's face it! Geoff can be bought over, especially when he feels important! Anyway, you go away from the meeting feeling more positive and perhaps subconsciously not so aggravated and aggressive towards the prosecution. This will give ET the opportunity some time in the near future to offer you a deal that you automatically snap up! It's a pretty negative thought, though.

'On another angle, maybe I am doing ET an injustice and Burns really meant what he said? It could be something he believes in? Maybe Geoff was afraid to speak up in case he could later be called as a witness? You said he went deathly pale in the court when they asked for his details; maybe he's in big trouble himself? Who knows anyone? Either way, unless he changes his mind and bucks up his ideas, he's well and truly flushed. Some McKenzie Friend he is! If he can't hear an informal chat in a small room containing the most crucial words spoken on your behalf, then he will be absolutely rubbish in a packed court room. From now we'll refer to him as simply "Deaf Geoff".'

Poor Matt, even his so-called friend wasn't a real mate after all! If I had told him what a shame it was that he hadn't asked Julia, it would only have added insult to injury. But I knew just by looking at him that he also realized Julia would have backed him up through thick and thin regardless.

In the meantime Matt telephoned everyone he could possibly think of, good honourable friends who all supported, believed and cared about him. In particular, he rang one couple whose children had attended primary school with Sam; we had known them forever! Or at least it seemed that long ago. Caroline and John were both intelligent, articulate and bloody brilliant when it came to computers. Voice recognition was a specialist area they had developed and practised long before ET and his cronies had even begun to understand it. So John was very interested in the audio aspect of this case, and he and Caroline read some of the files.

The next day Matt phoned a very clever criminal barrister based in the north of England, who together with two very forward-thinking northern solicitors would have been a great asset in representing Matt in court. The judge, however, continued to say no to new representation. Nevertheless, Matt relayed Tom Burns' comments to the northern barrister, who immediately said, 'The CPS should drop the case against you immediately, because one of their prosecution team has spoken to you in chambers. It is an abuse of process and they shouldn't carry on prosecuting knowing you are innocent!' It was extremely encouraging, coming from someone who really knew what he was talking about.

Looking at Matt I could see Geoff's betrayal was eating him up. You think someone is a very close friend but they turn out to be an enemy instead; it's a hard pill to swallow. Our other friends couldn't believe that Geoff had denied all knowledge of what would have been Matt's freedom pass.

Sam and Helen couldn't grasp the situation at all.

'Bloody hell, Mum! Deaf Geoff is really taking the pee this time! He's stayed with us and been welcomed as part of our circle and he is an absolute traitor! It sounds as though he is happy to assist the CPS and is helping them to try and put Dad away! What a bastard!'

Apparently Geoff hadn't understood the significance of his denial and had still thought we could be friends! I didn't get it. After all, he knew what Matt was going through first-hand, but when he could have done something to free Matt he denied anything had happened. I guess people do very strange things.

Thank goodness we knew people who were willing to help and Paul was one of them! He very kindly put together a document for Matt to go for a judicial review, which in

215

layman's terms meant that it wasn't fair for Matt to represent himself when a dismissal should be granted.

So on Friday 16th December Matt and I took the bus to The Aldwych, carrying two large files to hand in to the Royal Courts in The Strand. Crossing the very wide road I fainted, and was very lucky the busy traffic stopped in time. Matt had thought I was still walking by his side and was shocked to see me lying in the road. It took three kind American female tourists and Matt to lift me out of my trance-like state and put me on safe ground on the pavement. I'm not a big woman by any stretch of the imagination, but I was actually comfortable lying in the middle of the road as I thought I was in bed, and I was upset to find people trying to wake me! When I realized where I was I felt embarrassed and thanked them profusely for helping me.

I told Matt I was all right to go to the court and deliver the papers. It was very important that the court received the papers that afternoon as time was running out. Matt wanted me to stop and have a drink as I must have looked pretty shaken. I realized I had hurt my left knee as I could feel blood trickling down my leg. I was wearing trousers, though, and I wasn't about to roll up my trousers in the street to inspect the damage! I managed to hobble to the law courts and, before we went to the department to register the documents, I found an antiquated ladies room and stuffed loo paper around my knee to try and pad it. Because it was cut, the paper stuck to it quite easily. The area we needed to find was upstairs, then down-stairs; then there were yet more stairs across the building. I was very pleased when we finally found the correct department. We were fortunate for once to be near the front of a queue waiting to register, and it didn't take too long to go through the formalities. By the time we were back on The Strand and had crossed over to wait for a bus, I wasn't feeling very well. I telephoned Helen and asked her to make me an appointment with one of the excellent doctors at her local practice, which is two minutes from Helen's house. Helen rang back very quickly as she had managed to get me in to see a doctor in an hour, giving us just enough time to catch the bus back home.

I went direct to the doctor with Matt and she saw me almost immediately. She was very thorough, although she wasn't too bothered with my cut and grazed knee. No, she was more concerned with my blood pressure, or lack of it! I have always had low blood pressure, which seemed strange. You would have thought with all the terrible things happening to Matt that it would have been sky high! But it was so low that day that the doctor couldn't hear it at all! She tested it twice and said she wanted me to have a heart examination as soon as possible. So there I was, throughout the Christmas holidays, all wired up with a monitor and colourful wires in green, red and blue adding to my festive accessories! We were in Bournemouth at Kate and Keith's hotel and people kept coming over to ask me if I was ill. What did they think?

The contraption was on for seven days and just before New Year I went back to the hospital. Once they had taken all the wires off they said my heart seemed to be fine and that it was probably something called *vaso vagal*, which means passing out without warning. As usual they put it all down to stress. Let's face it, the Davidson family and stress were a double act, similar to The Two Ronnies, Morecambe and Wise, and peaches and cream.

I was obviously happy my heart wasn't an attack waiting to happen. But fainting in the road in the middle of town wasn't a prospect I looked forward to again either! I was really lucky the first time and must have had divine protection by whoever, whatever. Still, the chances of that happening again I shudder to think about! I decided to visit my wonderful Chinese surgeon friend Ming. She had helped me for years when conventional medicine had failed, and she gave me some natural herbs and gingseng. I began to feel better.

We had planned another mini break to Rome early in the New Year. Italian ice cream and the Trevi Fountain were calling us back to throw more coins in for good luck! After five days we felt much better. Rome is a wonderful, majestic city and just walking around the Colosseum, imagining Martin Clarke and Elliott Taylor being thrown to the lions, was invigorating!

In January 2007 there were a number of hearings, and a glimmer of hope concerning my mobile phone. Although I indicated earlier that I had put the phone incident on a back burner, it's never what you know, but very often who! Through our circle of friends, I was indirectly introduced to a company in the city that had been communicating with our computer voice recognition friend John. John had taken charge of the phone bugging situation and had emailed his comments to a technical audio expert, Ben Nicholls, who was working for this company. John told Ben my name and without telling him about the case explained that his friend Claire Davidson knew a defendant involved in a criminal case, and that owing to her conversation with this defendant on their mobiles, Claire's phone had been bugged. John's technical explanations helped my cause and Mr Nicholls arranged to meet me in a couple of weeks to go through the material, as he was very interested to hear the conversations and would give me his professional opinion.

As each defendant had his or her own agenda, which was highly confidential, I hadn't thought that Adrienne Carter would have told her solicitor Frances Reece about my mobile phone being bugged, but I suppose it was to do with her phone call to me, so it probably did get included in her day-to-day counsel conferences. Frances Reece spoke to me about the mobile phone, and I said I was looking into it through a friend who understood technology and was very helpful to Matt and me.

She seemed interested and asked, 'How far have you got with finding out anything constructive?'

'Well, I haven't yet! But I'm having a meeting in the city next week, with someone who, fingers crossed, appears to have professional expertise and might be able to help me.'

'Have you considered who this man is? Or the company he works for?'

'I don't think I follow what you're saying, Frances?'

'You have to make sure there isn't a conflict of interest and that he isn't already employed on a consultancy basis by the prosecution and the Crime Squad!'

'Thank you, Frances. I honestly never gave it a thought! I'll check it out before I meet him.'

I phoned Ben Nicholls when I arrived home. He was very friendly, talking small talk, and then I introduced into the conversation that I was very loosely connected with the Matthew Carter case, and had he ever heard about it in his line of work? He paused, too long for my liking, and his voice completely changed from happy-go-lucky Ben to dull, distant, desperate Dan!

He actually spluttered down the phone and announced, 'I feel sick!'

I calmly asked him why, and he said he had been working on a daily basis on that case for the past couple of years for both the police and the prosecution, enhancing sound and whatever else was required of him in his technical capacity. I couldn't believe it! Out of all the employees working for this large organization, I chose out of a hat Ben Nicholls. As he sounded quite ill, scared, call it what you wish, in a strange way I felt sorry for him.

'I think you had better go to the local pub and order a very large drink!'

'Yes, Claire, I think I will. I'll speak to you soon.'

'Okay, take care!' I knew I would never speak to him again. I did try calling him once, but, of course, as soon as I told the operator my name she put me through to his personal voice message.

In the scheme of things and with all that was happening to my husband, the flaming phone could once again take a back seat to be dealt with at a much later date. But with this outburst from Ben Nicholls, Matt and I knew the tapes had been tampered with. We had probably known all along but this professional expert was the proof we needed. He'd actually admitted his major part in the case without realizing that if the case came to trial Matt would call him as a witness! Then he would be well and truly sick!

With the mobile phone locked up once again in a safe place, we concentrated on the January hearings. At one hearing in particular, Laura came with Leslie. I had to give her the benefit of the doubt again when she said, 'Leslie hasn't been anywhere lately and it's good for him to get out!' Perhaps she spoke without really thinking it through. What did she think this was, a fun day at Alton Towers? This was a Crown Court, her nephew was right smack bang in the middle of a huge prosecution case, and Laura knew how innocent Matt was, so why did she assume her very thoughtless comments weren't extremely hurtful? Regardless of the building society bond she had lodged at the court, I was becoming more and more aggravated by her!

Unfortunately for Leslie, the hearing was a bit of a letdown, as the morning was spent for the majority of the time in the court foyer, due to the judge needing to pass sentence on other defendants in a couple of cases that were being heard before our major case could commence. Matt was used to it. Leslie wasn't, and by lunchtime when nothing of any significance had happened and the judge had said that the court would reconvene after 2 p.m. Laura and Leslie wanted to go home. Matt told them where the nearest station was and left them to it! I don't know if they expected Matt to drive them back to north west London, but it wasn't going to happen. He wouldn't have had enough time to get back to south London, and it wasn't Matt's problem. He hadn't asked Laura and Leslie to come to court, it had been Laura's idea for her husband to get out of the house!

Another hearing the following week was very different, as Julia came with us this time. Her views on the entire case were as open and straightforward as only Julia could be! She sat next to Matt and Jennifer Thornton in the gallery, and after about an hour of listening to what she described as total rubbish, she came and sat with me.

'Claire! You are better off out here; it is all drivel! Silly schoolboy arguments between both counsel and we the public are paying for their lifestyle! I am sure this case is going to fall apart and there won't be a trial. If there is one, the entire jury will die of boredom! Either way Matt will be free, I feel very positive about it!'

For once we went home feeling positive and upbeat. Thank goodness for Julia!

January at the best of times is very busy for Matt. It's the end of the tax year, as all self-employed people know, and it seems that everyone comes out of the woodwork, especially when you switch the television on and there appears to be a total bombardment of advertising, advising one and all, 'Get your tax return in by 31st January or you'll receive a fine of one hundred pounds.' It's the same when you travel on a bus or drive your car, an enormous billboard looms down at you as you try to pass it and pretend you haven't noticed the tax words displayed as though it's the latest Oscar winning film starring Tom Hanks!

As Matt is one hundred per cent loyal to all his clients, everyone is treated with the same friendly respect. Matt's easy-going way makes everyone feel special and he takes away any fears they may have about their taxes. Unfortunately, this meant that the phones were ringing constantly. Many clients who worked unsociable hours called him later in the evening, including on Saturdays and Sundays. There is always a plus and a minus to whatever you do in life, and Matt's long hours were the price of working from home. So Matt was completely caught up with client paperwork and loads of legal papers. Cracks were beginning to show on my husband!

I could see the mood swings were not a part of his usual personality, but he had been tested to the brim and the stress was now beginning to overflow with a mixture of bottled up anger, frustration and hatred towards a number of individuals. He was literally dividing his life between work and the dreaded court case. More and more papers kept arriving from the CPS for Matt to read at the last minute, and now that he was totally on his own, without any McKenzie Friend and with a trial starting in early February, it was bloody amazing he could concentrate on his work at all!

Whatever pressures I could take away from him I did, but it was a very hard month to get through. No one outside our four walls will ever know, understand or appreciate how tough you need to be to come out of that and keep a small quality of sanity. Paul tried yet again to come to Matt's rescue. He was amazed that Matt was left high and dry to represent himself in such a high-powered, huge case. He made a few phone calls to legal colleagues and introduced us to Stephen Gilchrist, who is a very experienced solicitor in criminal law. After meeting Stephen and two barristers at a hotel in Brighton, Matt took to them immediately. There was a very good chemistry, and maybe finally, fingers crossed, Judge Benedict would agree to the new representation.

By the end of January I was having an outpatient test at the Royal Free Hospital in Hampstead. Before I went in for the test my mobile rang and it was Adrienne Carter. Her words were cryptic as she said, 'Don't ask me any questions, but Matt and I felt I should phone you to just say that it will be over very soon. I'll see you in court next week,' and she put the phone down.

I rang off with mixed feelings. Matt and I had learnt very quickly that hope and ET didn't go together. Whatever positive thoughts we had on entering the court building were usually dashed by the CPS quickly putting as many spokes as possible into every wheel. I told Matt when I arrived home about the call and he felt the same way as I did. The one voice keeping our hopes alive was Linda's. I know our friends, especially Julia and Clarence, continually told us over and over that Matt wouldn't go to trial and that he would be freed. But although they were spoken with a great deal of common sense and were very comforting, Linda's words weren't said simply in close friendship or because she had strong feelings for Matt and I. She always seemed to know what had happened in court without us telling her, and she continued communicating with us. 'There will be no trial and they all know Matt is innocent, so he will come out of this and be free. I am positive.' She got us through January just with a few simple words and a phone call.

21

On Monday 6th February we were met with the same old scenario: the same cameramen waiting outside the main entrance; the same Court, number 1; the same security staff sitting at the desk outside the court; the same hideous screens outside Court 1; the same prosecution room, with the same smiling, smirking squad of police and prosecution; the same journalists, with their notebooks and pens poised at the ready to be first to let their newspaper know the trial was going to start. Carol and Laura, knowing the pattern off by heart, thought it was probably the umpteenth time they had come to court with us to swear their oaths before trial. Plus there was a new counsel waiting in the foyer for Matt, as they were going to try to kick-start the morning agenda by putting their legal stance in front of the judge and hoping he had a change of heart.

Sitting once again outside Court 1, I watched with interest as the very smug prosecution counsel and Martin Clarke's merry men kept bringing trolleys of files into their room. They kept looking across at us; without saying a word I could read their minds. 'This time there will be no escape, no last minute shenanigans. We will all be highly commended, praised and honoured for our very skilful work together, with our extremely clever handling of such a major, complicated case!'

I sat in my usual seat and thought that one day we should donate a plaque to go outside Courts 1, 5 and 6. It would have embossed gold letters that would explain in very simple terms what we thought about our excessive year in, year out case. Of course, the words would probably be too rude for a public foyer!

The journalist who always spoke to Matt and occasionally chatted to me came over and seemed genuinely interested in Matt's innocence. Whether it was on the surface or not, it didn't matter. It was good to see a friendly face, even though he told me the other journalists couldn't understand why he bothered. They'd all put us in one big melting pot and labelled us all the same! I wasn't that upset at hearing negative words about us; I just felt that the men and women carrying their notebooks and pens weren't qualified to make a judgement. It was worrying that so-called professionals seemed interested only in appearances and not facts!

Once again I wished my husband good luck as he became lost in the middle of barristers' unflattering grey wigs and black gowns and bland policemen, queuing to be checked behind the screen before they went into the court room. This time he wasn't alone: Stephen Gilchrist and two barristers walked into court with Matt. I kept everything crossed.

I didn't have very long to wait, as although the senior barrister spoke extremely well in court and did his utmost to convince the judge that Matt needed representation, Judge Benedict dug his heels in and said, 'No, Mr Davidson will represent himself at trial.' The team were dismissed and the court took a break.

Stephen Gilchrist, a very mild-mannered man with a soft speaking voice, the complete opposite to Jack Sandler, expressed his concerns for Matt and couldn't understand why the trial judge was so determined to make Matt defend himself.

'It seems crazy, Matt. Let's see what happens today and tomorrow and keep us informed. Sorry we couldn't get anywhere.'

The two barristers and the solicitor left after that and Matt stood in the foyer looking bemused. Carol and Laura had completed their swearing of oaths, and were waiting to go back into court to see what the next point of discussion was on the agenda. The Carters' defence counsel were walking around commenting to Matt that they didn't understand the judge's reasoning. In fact, it seemed as though no one understood it, as the prosecution were also apparently against Matt representing himself! I thought quietly to myself, maybe it's a blessing in disguise? If the prosecution want Matt to have counsel, they must know that his inexperience will totally disrupt the court. Oh, I did hope so!

ET was rushing in and out of the court room with a spiteful smile on his face, making him look even more silly and superficial than usual! He was obviously a frustrated actor who pictured himself as larger than life. I suppose if he'd had a decent character I could have acknowledged him in a different light, but he appeared to be without any human kindness. It always amazes me when the least likely people think so much of themselves and people who deserve the recognition don't expect it at all!

By lunchtime it was decided that the next day would be crunch day, as Adrienne's surgeon who had saved her life a year ago was going to testify on her behalf. The prosecution and the National Crime Squad were conjuring up out of a hat a surgeon, who I suppose as a probable friend of ET or Martin Clarke would testify just the opposite! To swear blindly on oath that Mrs Carter had only suffered a mild attack of indigestion, when her operation scars showed a very different story, seemed a very pointless exercise.

Laura was as insensitive as ever when she came out of the court room with Carol. Carol was very different, though; whatever her thoughts were she kept them to herself. We went home, dropping off Laura first and telling her we didn't need her support the next day. We didn't expect Carol to go back to the court that week either, as she lived in Hertfordshire and had her own life to lead. Besides, we had Julia coming, to bring a fresh approach to the entire proceedings.

22

Julia wasn't a rumbustious personality by any means, but she was born under the sign of Taurus the Bull, so she was very definite in her ideas. She looked at life differently, which was a good thing because it meant that the conversation on the way to court the following morning seemed lighter. Although Matt wasn't exactly buoyant, he did appear more cheerful. As usual Sammy Davis Jnr's repertoire from 'Candy Man' to 'Birth of the Blues' was helping Matt to keep the faith, and by the time we reached the parking garage, we just had time for Matt's favourite track, 'I'm Not Anyone'. I think the parking attendant recognized our car by the music alone!

With Matt chatting amiably to Julia, I kept on wondering why the surgeons were being called. Why would that make a difference to a trial at this late stage, when Adrienne had been out of hospital for a year? There must be something going on that we weren't grasping! As we walked past the cameramen I whispered to Matt, 'They obviously don't know you are the infamous Dangerous Davidson, do they?'

'No, thank goodness!'

The court entrance seemed even busier that day than it had been the day before. There were more journalists, and the prosecution room was heaving with Crime Squad buddies. Even the prosecuting solicitor without a name was gracing us with his presence. ET was in deep conversation with William Channing, and Tom Burns, carrying files with Naomi Pearlman, looked very uncomfortable as he passed us. The Carters had all their counsel with them, Jennifer had hers, and

Matt had Julia and me! There were no legal eagles rushing around him offering valuable advice. But Matt looked well. Whether he was silently gearing himself up for a fight you couldn't tell; he was playing his cards very close to his chest!

Writing this book I don't think I can possibly explain what it's like to watch, as often as I have, my husband, whom I love dearly, go into a Crown Court room, representing himself in a case that has gone on since time began, and realize that the judicial system is all a game! The law is just hit and miss! You win some, you lose some! If you are lucky, you find a barrister capable of giving a powerful and dramatic performance in court. If, however, your barrister is still learning his or her craft, perhaps your only alternative is to represent yourself. All I know is that only the strongest survive, and I was willing Matt to survive.

The cast of hundreds went into court, they all came out, they went back in. It was one of those mornings. Julia sat in the public gallery but because of the screen she could hardly hear a word. She came out looking very unimpressed. There was another break, this time for quite awhile, as it appears that Adrienne's surgeon was away in the West Indies. The court were trying to arrange a video link with him for after lunch. The prosecution's surgeon had arrived and ET was escorting him to their conference room, no doubt briefing him on what to say!

Everyone was standing around chatting to each other, and Stuart Parry, Matthew Carter's solicitor, caught me looking very worried. 'Claire, do you think Matt knows what he is doing in court?'

'No, Stuart, I shouldn't think so for one moment!'

'Well, why doesn't he stand up, sit down, stand up again and protest strongly if he doesn't understand what the prosecution are saying? He's not doing himself any favours if he doesn't drive the court mad by continually standing up and throwing a spanner in the works! He's too nice!'

'I'll tell him what you advise and thank you, but I'm sure Matt will go for it when he's ready. I can assure you he won't let the prosecution walk all over him. Wait and see, Stuart.'

'Just tell him to get a move on. The judge needs to see that Matt is unable to represent himself!'

I thanked him again for his concern and walked back to Julia and Matt. At lunchtime Matt, Julia and I went to a local pub to talk about the morning's non-events. Obviously the court were no longer worried about Matt leaving the building without a legal escort! We saw Matthew Carter walking up and down the street near the court, having what appeared to be a very in-depth conversation on his mobile. He was always very immaculately dressed, and today was no exception, as I noticed his very modern cap and cashmere scarf partly covering his mouth, not so much to keep out the cold but probably to stop the press from taking his photo. It was impossible to detect what he was thinking. Ever since day one when the case had started he and Adrienne had always managed very professionally to cover up their true feelings!

We'd been given an extra long lunch hour while they were trying to sort out the video link for Court 2. Matt had even been told that I would be allowed in as well! How incredible! What a shame I didn't know sooner – I could have brought popcorn! Julia's point of view about the hearing so far was very interesting. I couldn't wait to see her reaction to the two surgeons in the afternoon, and I still didn't understand why the court was making such an effort so late in the day. A video link to the West Indies must cost huge bucks; it was very weird!

We left the pub and arrived back at the court before 2 p.m. Other than the security staff at the entrance, the entire foyer was like a graveyard; there wasn't a soul around! Weird, strange, peculiar, very odd indeed! We walked around to Court 1, but there wasn't anyone there either! The prosecution room door was open but that was also empty! There were no security guards sitting outside the court near the screens, because the screens had been taken away. It was as though we had been caught up in an Alfred Hitchcock mystery, a thriller where nothing is as it seems, no one is who they say they are, and if you rub your eyes you suddenly wake up to find it was just a terrible dream. No such luck in reality: four horrible years spent dreaming could only have meant we'd been in a bloody coma!

We left the Court 1 area and walked along the corridor to Court 2. Matt looked at his watch and commented, 'They must all be inside the court. Maybe they started early?'

Matt opened the door to Court 2; it was dark inside, deserted. No video link had been set up and there was no sign of anyone!

'Well, the canteen closes at 2 every day so it's not worth looking there. We'll have to sit outside Court 2 and wait for a sign of life to materialize from somewhere. But in all the years I've sat outside these court rooms I have never seen it like this. There isn't a wig in sight!'

Matt double-checked Court 1 again but it was still unattended. The three of us were bewildered. Before lunch the public area around Court 1 had been crowded. Two hours later there was not a soul in sight.

'Something's up! God knows what!' As I said it, we saw ET and Tom Burns walking quickly towards us.

'Mr Davidson, would you come into a conference room with us? We want to talk to you, and you can come in as well, Mrs Davidson.' ET pointed to a small room near Court 2.

Call it gut instinct, call it whatever you want, I know myself very well. If I'd taken part in a meeting with the prosecution and ET had said anything to Matt that I wasn't happy with, I would have lost it completely. So I just answered, 'No, thank you. Julia can go in with Matt instead of me.'

It was normal for me to sit outside whichever court room or conference room and I should have been used to it by now, but today was very different and emotionally I was all over the place! It was so quiet you could hear a pin drop. I was lost in my thoughts thinking the entire Crown Court was a morgue, when Matthew Carter came running along the corridor. As he ran past me, he called out, 'Claire! Everything will be all right very soon!' He never gave me a chance to answer him though!

As Matthew disappeared from view, Jennifer Thornton's mother, Pamela MacDonald, came walking towards me. She looked stressed, which was probably just how I looked.

'Do you know what's happening?'

'No, I haven't a clue. My husband and a close friend of ours have gone into a conference room with Elliott Taylor and Tom Burns from the prosecution.'

She looked at me blankly, because although her daughter was the third defendant, and Mrs MacDonald was a supportive mother, I had only seen Pamela at that court once before. She was therefore totally in the dark regarding barristers' names. There was nothing more to add; so she just said, 'I'll go and find Jenny.' We wished each other good luck and I waited patiently hoping something constructive would happen! I did wonder where Adrienne Carter was!

The conference door opened and I had never seen Matt look so angry. Julia walked quietly behind him and ET and Tom Burns walked away from us towards Court 1.

'I don't know what's been said to you, but Matthew Carter has just run past and shouted out that everything would be all right very soon. Judging by your angry face, though, I can see that's not the case. What happened?'

'You're absolutely right! Angry is putting it bloody mildly! We sat down in that room and ET spoke to me as though he was doing me a massive favour and a good turn rolled into one! He said that Matthew Carter is signing a deal and so is Jennifer Thornton. Adrienne Carter's name will stay on file but she doesn't have to go to trial because of her ill health.

He said they could offer me the same deal as they offered me last year when I was represented by Edward Miles. What it means is a soft conviction, but I'll be able to walk out of here! I told ET what he could do with that offer and he had the audacity to say that it was a really good deal! So I let rip, screaming my head off, which they weren't expecting. I asked both of them why I should do a deal when I hadn't done anything wrong in the first place. Pointing to Tom Burns, I told ET, last December, Burns had said 'I would love to defend you and of course we all know you are completely innocent.' ET rolled his eyes to the ceiling as Tom Burns nodded his head in silent agreement. Then ET put the icing on the cake by asking whether, if they let me go, I would promise not to go after them! I just looked at him in disgust and told him I would think about it!'

Julia looking very pensive at Matt's anger, and said, 'I noted their actions as well as the words spoken to Matt, so I thought I would throw in a question. I asked both of them why the Inland Revenue weren't being prosecuted for agreeing the accounts that Matt had submitted on behalf of Carter. Neither of them could answer me. They just looked blank!'

I looked from my husband to my friend. I was a little thrown by Matt's outburst, but I understood it fully. Obviously they'd all thought Matt was a pushover who would do exactly what they asked of him. What a surprise or shock they must have had when they'd realized you can only push him so far! He takes more than the average person, but when he does lose his cool, you need to be a million miles away. I was all of a sudden very pleased that Julia had gone into the conference room instead of me!

'So what happens now?'

'ET has gone into court to ask Judge Benedict if I can have temporary representation. I assume it will be Adrienne Carter's team as she no longer needs counsel. And then I suppose we will go to court and see what happens!'

'But that means you don't have a choice or a say in who represents you! That can't be right?'

Suddenly there was life outside Court 1. Matt, Julia and I walked back to where the noise came from and saw how crowded the prosecution conference room was. Even Martin Clarke had turned up! He must have been hiding in a back room somewhere and needed to be on show now for any reporter or journalist willing to listen to him. Jenny Thornton was with her mother in a conference room with the door open, talking quietly to her barrister and solicitor. And just like the genie in Aladdin's lamp, both Adrienne and Matthew Carter had materialized from nowhere. They were in deep conversation with their teams in the main area outside the court.

ET came running out of the court room and was buzzing around like a bumble bee ready to sting! Everyone seemed to be waiting for Judge Benedict to make some decisions. By that point the prosecution and the defence knew that Matt Davidson wasn't prepared, on any terms, to accept a deal with a soft conviction. There appeared to be admiration for Matt, as no one had believed he was such a definite, solid character. He certainly wasn't going to be pushed around anymore and his face showed it!

They all went into court and I phoned home and told Helen about her son's eventful afternoon. My poor mother-in-law! It must have been very difficult for her to comprehend what was happening to Matt. As usual I waited for everyone to come out to find out what else had happened! Adrienne Carter came out with her team and Jennifer Thornton with hers and we acknowledged each other. The journalist who had taken the time to talk to us and perhaps make up his own mind about Matt was having a one-to-one interview with Martin Clarke, who looked oh so pleased with himself. Matt came out with Julia and we left the court.

As we walked to the car, Matt's expression relaxed. 'I was

in the dock with the other defendants, and Matthew Carter couldn't understand why I looked so angry! I explained to him what had happened in the conference room and he called his solicitor Stuart Parry to come over to the dock. Matthew said, "I've signed a deal today that should have incorporated Adrienne, Jenny and Matt. He should be totally free, yet he tells me a different story. What's going on? I want you to sort it out!" Stuart Parry, obviously trying to calm him down, said, "Don't worry, it will all be okay." I don't think I believe him at all, I don't trust any of them! It seems Matthew Carter wanted to believe in them, but it appears everyone is trying to fool each other.'

'I'm not surprised, are you, Matt? Anything to do with ET and Martin Clarke is bound not to have a decent outcome!'

'No. I agree with you, Claire, and so Matthew Carter and Jennifer Thornton have to appear at the Old Bailey next month, The judge wouldn't let Matthew spend time at home with Adrienne and Jazmin; he said Matthew had to stay in custody for the month and that it was inevitable he would then receive a prison sentence. Adrienne is free, if you can call it that! With ET hovering around, freedom is not an easy word to use! Tomorrow we have to go to Frances Reece's office as she has a couple of weeks spare on her hands, now the case is over for Adrienne, and I have been granted temporary representation. I think Greg Lawrence the junior barrister is going to represent me, so we'll see what they say tomorrow.'

Arriving at the solicitor's office in the City the next morning, we found that Frances Reece didn't seem too happy about having Matt as her temporary client. But Greg Lawrence sitting at the long boardroom table appeared as relaxed as usual. Smiling broadly at us he looked towards me and said, 'You really caused the prosecution to hop up and down during the case, Claire!'

I looked at him and answered, 'I did? Why? How?'

'Oh, don't make out you don't know! Obviously all the letters you wrote, the emails you sent, the people you saw The CPS are not used to it. Good for you!'

'Greg, I never set out to make anyone from the prosecution think I liked them, why would I? Surely other wives husbands or partners have done the same as I have?'

'Not to the extent that you have!'

'Oh well, there's always a first!'

Frances was looking at Matt without her usual amicable smile. 'What exactly do you want me to advise you with Matt?'

'Well, as you know, I have been representing myself since last June, and in December I was invited to attend an informal meeting at Elliott Taylor's chambers. I sat with Tom Burns and he told me they all knew I'm innocent and that he would love to defend me! Since that day I have spoken to a barrister who knows about the case and he said the prosecution should have dropped the charges against me immediately! But they chose to ignore what was said and instead Taylor offered me a soft conviction. I am supposed to shake his hand on this wonderful deal, but there's no way! I'm not interested!'

I watched Frances Reece's body language whilst Matt was talking and I didn't like the way she looked at both of us. Her attitude and her demeanour were totally different than when she was representing Adrienne. I didn't expect anything from her and neither did Matt, so it wasn't a surprise when she said, 'I don't really see what you expect me to do! The way see it, you have two choices: you can take the deal or you can stand trial alone.'

Matt and Frances seemed to glare at each other and Matt finally said, 'The choices you've offered me I don't need, so if I have to, I'll go to trial and I'll carry on representing myself.'

Both Greg and Frances wished him good luck and said if they could offer him any help he should contact them. To be fair, temporary representation had been granted the day before without the solicitor, barrister and Matt having the opportunity to agree. He'd been simply shoved across to them, and they were supposed to deal with the situation accordingly just because ET and the court said so!

We walked out and although Matt had been without counsel for almost nine months, he was now well and truly on his own! The case around the Carters had finished and Matt was now facing solo trial; it was absolute madness! But looking at him I could see he was determined to clear his name and walk out of the court a free man, not someone pandering to the prosecution's demands and accepting a third-rate deal that would inevitably go pear-shaped and tarnish Matt's name for life! I realize that the majority of you don't know my husband, but he is one hundred per cent squeaky clean, which is why he was so easily used by the police and the prosecution. It's a rotten business, but knowing him as well as I do, he will get through it! You never know, maybe what comes round will go around one day.

Matt called his trusted solicitor friend Paul and told him what had happened. Paul spoke to Stephen Gilchrist, who called another meeting, and once again it was agreed that Stephen and counsel would apply to the court for representation. In the meantime Matt complained to the Law Society about Jack Sandler and Edward Miles, and he received a letter from Sandler's legal practice saying they would look into the complaint, having realized that all communication among barrister, solicitor and client had completely broken down a long time ago. That letter was given to Judge Benedict, who was at that period of time working temporarily as a High Court judge for six months at the Old Bailey. The ambience was entirely different to the modern South London Crown Court; the Judge wasn't addressed as Your Honour anymore, he was called My Lord, and even the garments worn by the judges were more austere.

Matthew Carter had to appear at the Old Bailey and was

sentenced for seven years, because the deal he had apparently signed meant that he had admitted to one count out of the many counts that had originally been against his name. Jennifer Thornton was fined a small sum of money, but escaped a prison sentence. So that was the end of the Carter case and the beginning of Matt Davidson's fight for freedom!

A hearing was called by ET in March and Matt, together with his solicitor Stephen Gilchrist and Lewis Power the barrister, went to the High Court. The entrance to the public gallery was at the side, down a dark alleyway; it was very Victorian and very off-putting. I counted the stairs there were so many, 240 to be exact. By the time I reached the top, security said they didn't need to check me as I looked as though I shouldn't be there! I've heard that before! They told me that if I had to go to court again I should speak to the security at the front of the building, who would take me to a lift. They were very helpful and kind, which is a comfort when you visit a court like the Old Bailey.

I sat in a small public area along with a couple of security personnel who kept check on the gallery. In a glass dock sat my husband, a lone figure with a security guard sitting behind him. I felt sadness so intense it's impossible to put it into words. This is for real, I thought. Matt has been through so much and now he is facing a trial, possibly in this historical old court building, when the biggest and longest ever gang-land prosecution case has already finished. My husband is standing his ground and dealing with the dreaded court system on his own!

The barrister had his notes ready to speak on Matt's behalf and Stephen carried documents. ET and William Channing were shuffling their papers in front of Judge Hugh Benedict, who was dressed in the traditional black. Looking around the court room I shivered at my dark thoughts. This place had seen and heard so many gruesome cases that ended with the gallows and I felt as though Matt had been suffering a living death since 2003. My husband is a very brave and remarkable man!

The judge, having read the letter copied to him from Matt's previous solicitor's practice, agreed that representation was now necessary, and added that he hadn't realized the difficulties Matt had endured in not being able to communicate with his former team. So, finally, Stephen Gilchrist and his legal team were appointed, with Lewis Power the very amicable Irish barrister. On one hand this was very good news for Matt, but on the other, if the judge thought a trial was unnecessary he hadn't said anything, leaving the stage free for ET to put his ten pence worth in the pot.

'First of all, My Lord, let me say on behalf of the court thank you for allowing Mr Davidson representation.' ET waffled on and on about dates for the trial.

I wanted to put the black cap on my head and push ET in the dock, telling him loudly and clearly, 'You will be taken from this place straight to the gallows where you will hang for using innocent people in past cases, and for being such a revolting individual during this case!'

No such luck! ET, loving the sound of his voice, kept turning towards Matt, asking him if dates in the summer suited him. It sounded ridiculous, as though they were planning a party! The judge interrupted ET and said it could not be before September as the judge was there for six months, and would only be back at the south London court in September.

'Very well, My Lord. Mr Davidson, I think the week of 17th September is clear, so we'll pencil in that date and assume the trial will last for two weeks.'

Stephen was writing everything down and I was making my notes up high in the balcony. Then that was the end of the hearing.

By the time I had walked down the 240 stairs again, Matt

and Stephen were outside. The three of us went for a coffee, but Lewis had to get back to his chambers. Matt seemed in fairly good spirits, all things considered.

'Claire, on my way out ET was talking to Dick Warner, one of Martin Clarke's henchmen. He asked me who I planned to call as a witness, and I immediately said I would call him. He looked pretty flustered and told me that he would be busy with another trial at the time, so William Channing would be handling my case. I ignored him and repeated, "I'm calling you!" He said, "I won't be here!", but I just reiterated, "You!" and I continued staring at his horrible smarmy face as I repeated "You". He asked who else I would call. "Definitely Martin Clarke." Dick Warner made a face and said, "Clarke would be retired by then." I answered, "No problem, he can come out of retirement to go on the stand", and when ET asked if there would be anyone else, I added, "Tom Burns, add him to the list!" ET shook his head, saying, "No, he can't come as he'll be at the same trial as me!" But I just said, "I'm calling Burns, Clarke and you!" as I walked out of the court.'

'Bloody marvellous! Great timing, Matt.'

Over coffee Stephen suggested a tentative timetable for meetings and also a day for the collection of all the files at our house. It was a huge task he had to prepare Matt's case in such a short period of time. So the files were taken away within a day and Stephen set to work very quickly. Matt had various meetings at his office and sometimes I was actually allowed to go in with him. Both Matt and I liked and respected Stephen Gilchrist's and Lewis Power's intelligence and capabilities. Stephen remarked to Matt that he thought his endurance was amazing. He said that he'd had clients in the past who simply couldn't hack it and would have cracked under pressure or taken an overdose rather than go through what Matt had!

We stayed in touch with Journalist Jim – that's what I'm calling him. He was a likeable man and seemed genuinely interested in Matt's case. He came to a meeting we had with Stephen in a hotel in town, and gave us his input on the situation. It's always good to get another person's point of view, and we had a great deal of time for him. Matt felt confident in his legal team for the first time, and, with Paul's help as well, Matt was a very different person in April 2007 to the one who had been taken away at the end of April 2003!

23

Two months on, and Stephen had prepared the groundwork and done his homework. Together, he and Lewis Power, the straight-talking, charismatic barrister, made a very formidable team who were finally on the right track. Stephen also introduced Matt to Iain Wilson and Andrea Storey, two very bright younger colleagues who worked with him at his practice. They learnt a great deal from Stephen's expertise. They were nit-picking all the files with fine toothcombs; they worked in an exceptional, professional way and it was good for Matt to see the difference compared to the others before them. This time his team were working with him and for him, not against him!

Stephen had written to the prosecution bombarding them with questions. He asked Elliott Taylor and Tom Burns to either acknowledge or deny their words spoken to Matt in December 2006 and February 2007. Stephen's letters were ignored. He thought their actions were ridiculous as their silence told him everything. How stupid of them! Between Stephen and Iain they cleverly began digging under the prosecution's skin!

Eventually a lengthy reply came to Stephen's office that contained absolute nonsense from the anonymous and incognito prosecuting solicitor, the one who had originally been afraid to speak out. He signed his name Raymond Atkins. It appeared the Crown Prosecution were throwing the kitchen sink at Matt. Stephen emailed us a copy of Atkins' letter: it was laughable as they had pulled out of the bag so many counts against Matt they had put him on a par with Jack the Ripper, Al Capone and all the Great Train Robbers put together! They had stuck more than thirty counts on Matt; it was ridiculous! They obviously believed in their own publicity and inflated egos and thought anything they said and did would be acceptable. It wasn't! They wanted to deter Matt from carrying on with the case and believed that with the right amount of pressure he would still sign a deal.

There were two hearings at the Old Bailey during the summer. The first one on 14th June was an application for a stay of proceedings. It was very brief as Judge Benedict adjourned the preparatory hearing until 20th July. His reasons were that he needed to hear evidence from both the prosecution counsel and the defendant and his witnesses to the conversations on 13th December 2006 and 7th February 2007. At the second hearing in July, Lewis had to be at another trial and couldn't attend. He sent, let's just say, a less experienced young barrister in his place, and as Matt wasn't required to attend the court he waited in a restaurant around the corner from the Old Bailey. I went with Julia, without the stairs this time thank goodness! I made notes and saw Stephen and this new barrister in court and also Journalist Jim sitting behind Stephen. We had kept him informed of any hearings. I watched his face and Stephen's as the barrister working for Lewis proved to be not very helpful: he mumbled his words, he hadn't come prepared, and, maybe through no fault of his, his answers weren't effective.

ET was now taking a calculated back seat from the case, and his clone William Channing had taken over. But if I closed my eyes it was definitely a case of follow my leader, as WC sounded exactly the same as ET. The trial judge listened attentively to WC.

'My Lord, there is no reason for Elliott Taylor and Tom Burns to come to court. It's completely unnecessary for you and them, My Lord, and they will not waste their time with witness statements, as it is our view that the court will decide at Mr Davidson's trial. Therefore, we will not be complying with the defence's continued requests for my learned colleagues to testify in court or go to Mr Gilchrist's office before September. I am sure you will agree with me, My Lord, that regardless of what Mr Davidson says there were no witnesses to the remarks he claims were made!'

Julia's expression was a picture of anger. If she could have climbed over the top of the gallery I believe she would have. 'Do you think the judge will notice me if I raise my hand? I want to tell him the prosecuting barrister is speaking a load of rubbish. I was there and I am a witness!'

The judge seemed to take all WC's lies on board and answered quietly, 'Quite so, Mr Channing. I take it I am to understand that neither Mr Taylor nor Mr Burns will be giving evidence in court, as the CPS say it isn't necessary?'

The hearing finished after that. Julia and I looked at each other because today had definitely gone in the prosecution's favour. The young barrister for the defence had been quite ineffectual! We needed Lewis and quick! When we met Jim outside the court he voiced his opinion that he didn't think it looked too good! But as practical Stephen said, 'We have to wait and see.'

When we met up with Matt at the restaurant and told him about bloody Channing's comments, he said it would be all right! Stephen, a very likeable man and not one to make false promises, looked more perturbed than Matt, and Julia still carried on saying, 'It will all fall apart!'

By early August I had an idea! I sent an email to Stephen explaining that when Matt had come out of the meeting last December with Tom Burns and Deaf Geoff, the first thing he'd done after phoning me was to phone as many other people as possible, friends, clients, even a northern barrister. Surely if Matt was making the entire story up, he would need psychiatric help! No one in their right mind would suggest falsely that a prosecuting barrister of all people would say such revealing things! If Stephen agreed, Matt could draw up a list of the people he'd phoned and perhaps they would all write witness statements to what was said to them? They wouldn't speak to each other to agree a 'story' because they all came from different walks of life.

Anyway I wrote to Stephen and waited for a response from him. His one-line email followed very quickly, reading simply, 'Claire, excellent stuff! This could be the key. I'll call you later.'

Stephen and Iain contacted all the people Matt had listed, approximately thirty. By the middle of August there were enough statements from intelligent, articulate, professional people who had no reason to lie. They all told Stephen exactly the same story. So, together with very clever input in Stephen's legal terms, the statements were sent direct to Judge Hugh Benedict and the prosecution.

At the end of August we decided at the last minute to speak to our very reliable travel agent friend Allan. We had never been to Florence and as we loved Italy a long weekend sounded very good to both of us: beautiful architecture, the wonderful Duomo and the Uffizi Gallery, the Ponte Vecchio with its jewellery shops and loads of delicious gelato. It all sounded magical. Allan waved a magic wand and we packed our case in a few hours and temporarily forgot our problems. We didn't talk about ET or the court; we just took in fabulous Florence and agreed to return when Matt was a free man.

In early September, refreshed from our short break, we went with Helen to a wedding in Manchester. We sat at a table with ten people we had never met before, everyone chatting amicably to each other. No one talking to Matt, Helen or I would have known for one moment that they were sitting with Dangerous Davidson who was going to trial in just over two weeks. It's amazing what masks we wear when we have to! We spent two extra days in the north and

Helen enjoyed the change of scenery. When we arrived back, Matt wrote a list of witnesses he was determined to call, which included Ben Nicholls, the nervous audio technical expert. We really didn't know why he'd sounded so afraid on the phone, unless of course he'd known the work he was doing wasn't exactly straightforward. If he was on the stand swearing an oath, he would need to be truthful.

On Thursday 13th September there was a short hearing back at the south London court as Judge Benedict had finished his temporary assignment at the Old Bailey. It felt very strange walking into the court building and seeing Matt's name on the electronic notice board with a case number against him as though he was a prominent player. Through-out the Carter case Matt was always at the bottom of the list as he'd been more of an afterthought. Now he was the leading man!

As I was a definite witness I had to carry on sitting outside the court room, Court 5. It didn't take too long and Matt, Lewis and Stephen came out smiling, which was a good sign.

'Claire, at the beginning of the Carter case they invented four counts against me. Then, as you know, the prosecuting solicitor said it had miraculously climbed to the magic number thirty-two. Well, now it's gone down to eleven. I swear they pick the numbers out of a hat! The judge kept throwing out the extra counts they are trying so hard to pin on me, and he asked William Channing how long he felt the trial would take. Channing said four weeks. The judge asked why, when they originally said it would be two weeks maximum! Channing struck an ET pose and said they had many issues to go through that needed the extra time. The judge didn't com-ment any further after that.'

'Matt, are you okay with the despicable way the CPS are hell-bent on giving you a rough ride?'

'I feel confident in my innocence. I'll know I'm telling the truth, and they won't! Plus I'm looking forward to putting bastards like Martin Clarke, Elliott Taylor and Tom Burns on the stand. If I had my way I would call Deaf Geoff as well, so yes, I'm prepared mentally for this!'

To be honest I don't think I was!

By Monday 17th September I was thinking how quickly the time had gone since ET had set the trial for six months' time. Driving back to South London early Monday morning, Matt turned off and listened to Sammy Davis Jnr. Accompanying Matt and me was our daughter Sam. She was going to sit in the public gallery and support her father for as long as it took! Julia was coming to sit outside the court with me and Aunt Laura had to swear her oath, so she was travelling with us as well. Carol had been excused today as she'd sent a letter a few weeks before advising the court that she and Mike would be at their villa in Greece in September. She had pledged her oath earlier.

Matt had received loads of text messages from friends wishing him good luck and he'd brought a card to court from Carol and Mike. It read, 'All the good luck in the world, we're with you all the way. Lots of love, Carol and Mike.' It was very encouraging and kept our faith alive that decent human beings still existed.

We went to the canteen and met Matt's team, plus two clerks from Stephen's office who were there it seems to boost Matt's confidence should a trial take place! They'd also brought along a pretty paralegal student, Hayley Mahan, who had written out a witness statement, which she handed to us to read. She'd listened to the audio tapes and she stated, 'I have been listening to the audio conversations and comparing them with the transcripts compiled by the CPS, and whilst listening to a small handful, I have noticed various inaccuracies and misrepresentations; there are missing parts of the transcript and incorrect audio timing.' She was a very sweet girl and her statement was helpful. She also had a dig at Sandler and co, as she wrote, 'It would appear that our predecessors have not noticed any of the inaccuracies on the audio.' This was helpful too. Matt and I hadn't thought for one moment that the CPS and National Crime Squad had listened to it either! So what had Mr Nicholls been doing all the time he was employed as the audio expert consultant?

When they all went into court I had Julia's company to stop me from thinking too much. It seemed a long day to me not knowing what was happening! Journalist Jim was there and he spoke encouraging words to us and more importantly Lewis Power told Matt, 'We know you're innocent so let's see what happens today with the judge.' It was good for Matt to hear those words from his defence counsel. Even though he had heard it from the prosecuting barrister, he had never had a team who were on his side before.

When Sam and Laura eventually came out of the court with Jim clutching his notebook, Laura announced for the last time, 'There is definitely going to be a trial! You can see by the way the judge is speaking to the prosecution.'

I wanted to hit her! Sam burst into tears and said, 'Thank you, Auntie, you are a great comfort to have around! I don't want to hear your opinion!'

Jim, being a journalist whose job it was to notice everything, made a quiet sarcastic remark as he had a very good memory and had seen and heard Laura's exit from a court room before! Julia ignored her comments and comforted Sam by saying quite the opposite about her father, and that Laura is someone who often says hurtful things without thinking! I couldn't wait for Matt to come out of this and prove Laura wrong.

With Laura in the car we all kept quiet. After we had dropped her home first, Matt said, 'The judge spoke about the jury to William Channing. He told the Crown Prosecution that if the trial starts it will be on Wednesday and the jury will be sworn in then! The CPS included the horrible Naomi Pearlman working alongside WC. They both smiled happily at Judge Benedict's words as they brought their trolleys of files into court, and when they left they were laughing with two of the police, Dick Warner and Gary Porter. We have to be in court early again tomorrow as the judge will make his decision in the morning.'

Just as we pulled up outside Julia's flat, she said to Matt, 'I feel very positive that there won't be a trial, and Clarence has said it all along. So I'll speak to Claire tomorrow or ring me when you come out with good news.'

I couldn't wait to get home and get the vision of the court and Matt sitting in the dock out of my head. I thought our daughter was very brave to sit in the public gallery and listen to a load of rubbish spoken by the prosecution about her father.

Sam came back with us as we were going out with Helen for dinner. We gave Helen an update and I looked at my mother-in-law and realized she should have been in court instead of her sister. I asked her if she felt she could come with us tomorrow and sit with Sam in court. It would be just the four of us as Julia wasn't able to come the next day.

Helen didn't pause for a second, 'Of course I'll come with you. It is my son after all.' She rang Laura and told her, 'It's not necessary for you to come to the court tomorrow. I'm going to support my son.' Judging by the silence at the other end of the phone, I don't think Laura thought much of Helen going instead of her! I felt very pleased that Matt's mother was coming, though. She would maybe bring him the good luck he so desperately needed and deserved.

24

Tuesday 18th September was crunch day! I felt comforted that Matt's mum was with us as this was a very tense time. The canteen was once again very busy, and Lewis greeted my mother-in-law with kind words in his usual considerate manner. Thank God we had him as the barrister and not Miles! Stephen had been called away to deal with another urgent case outside London, but he'd sent his apologies and made sure Matt had enough substitutes in his place. He'd also left word for us to call him immediately we had a result.

I kissed Matt good luck as he went into court. Helen and Sam followed with Jim and his notebook. I watched the awful foursome with their fabricated files go into court: William Channing, Naomi Pearlman, Dick Warner and Gary Porter, a wonderful combination of police and prosecution. I heard one of them say 'four years' just loud enough for me to hear. It could only mean they hoped Matt would serve four years for a crime he hadn't committed! I wasn't about to take the bait, though. I didn't take any notice and carried on writing my notes.

It couldn't have been more than two minutes later when Matt and his counsel, followed by Helen, Sam and our new friend Journalist Jim, came out of the court. The prosecution and the police pulling their trolleys of files came out soon after and went into a side room. It seems that the clerk of the court had apologised to everyone on behalf of the judge, who had apparently forgotten he had a doctor's appointment that morning and had been unable to cancel it. Therefore, the hearing had been delayed until midday.

There wasn't anything to do but go and have a coffee. Matt fancied getting out of the building, so Jim suggested a small café not too far away. For an hour we talked about everything else we could think of and the time went very quickly. By 11.30 we made our way back to the court, walking slowly. We were outside Court 5 in good time, and there was Matt's counsel leading the way in, with the ghastly Crown Prosecution and Crime Squad following. Hand on heart I promise you, I was just about to begin writing when everyone came straight back out again! I remembered that in the Carter case there had been many delays over the years, so many that it sometimes seemed the barristers spent more time chatting in the corridor than in the court room. But this was very strange as the judge wasn't even back yet! There were more apologies and we were all told to take a long lunch. The hearing would start at 2 p.m.

Jim had to get back to his office, but knowing Matt's love for Italian food he directed us to an Italian restaurant and wished Matt good luck, saying that he would be in touch. The four of us sat and picked at our food. We weren't particularly hungry as the judge's non-appearance in court only seemed to prolong the agony for Matt. Sam looked as though she could have killed someone and Helen just looked very tired.

Whatever small talk conversation we had, we all realized Matt's thinking pattern must be in turmoil, even though he looked outwardly calm. Bloody good acting, Matt had missed his vocation. He should have won an Oscar for his performance. You have to be a very special person to deal with the dud hand of cards dealt to him by the prosecution counsel, who together with the police had conjured up an abusive process of fiction that they were desperately trying to make fact! The prosecuting barristers were all the same: they came from the same charm school; they spoke in the same smug, smarmy, self-obsessed manner; and the way they had conducted themselves during the past few months was beyond words! I don't know what Matt was thinking walking back to the court, but I was imagining a doll with me sticking pins in it!

At 2 p.m. everyone filed back into the court room and I watched the door. Sure enough, within a minute they all came out again! Whatever the judge's reasons for another delay, they must have been affecting my husband's health! You wouldn't know it, though, as he was smiling with his team. As Helen and Sam weren't used to the precarious court timetable, they seemed a little nervous, which under the circumstances was justified. Apparently Judge Benedict was in chambers, but he required another thirty minutes to prepare his notes before starting the hearing.

Today was beginning to feel like a washout! Poor Matt! How can he smile at a time like this? I had to give Lewis Power credit for probably helping Matt to see the funny side of the court system. There are many people who without realizing it take away your energy, while others give energy out. Lewis was definitely the latter; plus his confidence and positive approach were a great boost for my husband. I know how strong Matt is mentally. It's just very difficult to reason rationally when you arrive at the court and see the wigs of the Crown Prosecution and the crime squad all conspiring to make you suffer because you dare to challenge them and their lies!

At 2.30 they were all called in again and this time I knew after five minutes that the judge was there and that Matt was sitting in the dock listening to the judge's direction as to whether to go to trial or not! Helen and Sam must have been feeling very tense; it cannot have been pleasant listening to a judge talk about your son or your father. I'm not sure who had it worse – me out in the corridor on my own trying to keep calm, or those sitting in the court room.

I paced up and down the corridor. I must have worn the leather out on my shoes walking up and down trying to prepare myself for whatever the court was planning. I visualized Martin Clarke waiting at the end of a phone to hear good news from his merry men that the prosecution case against Matt Davidson would begin tomorrow and last for a month.

Just before 3 p.m. I decided I couldn't wait any longer and I walked to the other end of the building, near Court 1, where the Carter trial had nearly happened. I called Kate in Bournemouth, and I remember her saying, 'Claire, no news is good news.' Then I happened to look through the glass swing doors and right down the far end I saw my mother-in-law's outline. She was looking for me, calling loudly, 'Claire! He's free! He's free!'

I have no idea what I said to Kate after that, I just remember my heart pounding as I ran like mad straight past Helen to find Matt. He was standing outside Court 5 and I'll never forget how happy he looked. Sam was crying good tears and I just felt euphoric. Lewis came out of the court and we all had a group hug. Helen joked, 'Very nice daughter-in-law I have! I rush out of the court especially to tell her the good news and she ignores me as though she is running a marathon!'

'Sorry, Helen, I wasn't sure I was hearing you correctly.'

It was pointless asking Matt questions at that moment. He was sitting in a conference room with Lewis with the door open and they were going over formalities. We couldn't thank Lewis enough and Stephen as well. It was a shame he couldn't be at court that day to see first-hand Matt beat the Crown Prosecution and the police. Journalist Jim missed it too. He'd probably assumed he had plenty of time to return to the court tomorrow for the start of Matt's trial.

Gary Porter from the Crime Squad came out of the court. He went over to Matt and shook his hand. He wanted to

253

shake my hand too. Usually I would have thought, Oh what the heck, just get it over with, but I stopped myself and turned my back on him! I didn't want to shake anyone's hand who an hour ago had been taking part in a plan to put Matt in prison for a crime he hadn't committed. All they had done was cost the public huge amounts of money and given us years of anguish. Even as I write this I dread to think how many other innocent men and women had their lives ruined by Martin Clarke and Elliott Taylor. If they had their way, Matt would have gone to prison for four years for absolutely nothing, just so they could have had their glory. In their minds, it would have justified the almost five years of hell they put my husband through. But as the trial judge had really put them in their place and Matt was a free man it made a complete mockery of him being there from day one!

Matt and Lewis finished their conversation and made a date to finalize the papers and collect his passport. He read his congratulatory texts from Stephen, Iain and Andrea who made up his legal team. They were all sorry not to be there with Lewis to witness Matt and the defence counsel's huge win.

I phoned Linda, who wasn't surprised in the slightest. 'I said all along there wouldn't be a trial, but Matt has been through a terrible ordeal and it will take time for him to get over it.'

Matt sent a text to Carol and Mike in Greece and he spoke to Paul who said, 'Within moments of Matt coming out of the court room it had spread through the legal walls like wild fire that he was free and had beaten the Crown Prosecution.'

Elliott Taylor must really have felt off-colour that night. After all, he could have saved himself the embarrassment by letting Matt go last February, but no, he chose to be bloody-minded and pig-headed. He thought he and his crew were untouchable, but Matt had called his bluff and Taylor had lost the plot, lost his crown and lost the case.

The four of us were on cloud nine and Sam and Helen told

me what had happened in court. Whenever the judge had paused in giving his ruling Sam had held her breath and dug her nails hard into Helen's hands. The marks were still prominent. Judge Hugh Benedict had magnificently reeled the prosecution in as bait and, wham, had caught them in a trap. That's my interpretation anyway, and apparently once the judge had read his ruling, Sam and Helen were out of their seats and Matt was out of the dock like lightning. Ethics didn't come into it at all, and Judge Benedict turned a blind eye, letting the three Davidsons leave the court to celebrate. That was a very decent thing for the judge to do, as the done thing in a court room is to wait for the judge to leave first.

We walked out of the court building for the last time. It was the most incredible feeling. The strain had simply vanished from Matt's face and his happiness was contagious. We all walked to the car park a very different foursome from the people who had arrived early that morning.

Driving from South London to our home, we listened to Sammy Davis Jnr and the track called 'I'm Not Anyone'. It had inspired Matt throughout the terrible years and we played it over and over again. We listened to it with renewed interest, as it's on a par for us with Frank Sinatra's 'My Way'.

I would love to tell you the words of the song but due to copyright, I'm not allowed. I'm sure Sammy wouldn't mind, but sadly he isn't here for me to ask, and I don't fancy getting in to trouble with American music moguls and finding myself in an American courtroom. All I can say is, I suggest to anyone going through a negative period, or having to deal with a bloody horrible time in their lives, to grab a copy and listen intently to every single inspiring word.

It's poignant, deeply moving and ticks all the correct boxes. And without actually repeating any part of the song, it encourages you to believe in yourself. The words are very meaningful as we all take our freedom for granted when it's actually a priceless gift.

That evening was spent having an impromptu dinner at a very pretty Italian restaurant overlooking a golf course. It was time to celebrate and the evening was going to be the first of many. It would soon be Matt's sixtieth and a big party of old and new friends, including the legal team and their partners, were all being invited to Kate and Keith's hotel in Bournemouth. We were going to have a great birthday weekend that we would always remember, and do our best to forget the bad times.

Looking back at Judge Benedict's ruling, which we have read many times, it seems clear that he ridiculed the prosecution and the case against Matt. To sum up, he said, 'I was considerably surprised that neither of the prosecuting counsel involved in the conversations of 13th December 2006 and 7th February 2007 were going to be called to give evidence, nor make witness statements, nor make themselves available for interview with the defence, and for me to continue would bring the administration of justice into disrepute. I find the leading counsel's offer of a discontinuance of proceedings upon an undertaking by the defendant not to bring an action in the civil courts the more disturbing and pernicious. It is clearly established that the court should be reluctant to stay proceedings except in exceptional circumstances.'

'Wow.' When His Honour Judge Benedict said the words 'disturbing' and 'pernicious' he was referring to the one and only Elliott Taylor, leading counsel and master of pig-headedness. After years of mental torture and turmoil, the words spoken by the trial judge were as inspiring to Matt as Sammy's song.

Obviously he thought Matt was the exception to the rule. The ruling was lengthy so I have just taken out an excerpt to give you the general idea. It's a piece of writing that should be in history books, as it is very well written and could be used as a caution against future prosecution cases that get out of hand. Especially if the counsel involved screw up because they want to win so badly they're prepared to turn lies into truth and fiction into fact.

I wrote to the judge thanking him. Whether he read it or not, I don't care! I felt grateful and I wanted to express it in writing.

A few weeks later, on a complete whim, Matt and I, together with Julia, decided to pay a visit to Deaf Geoff. Don't ask me why we did this, we just wanted to see if we could tie up any loose ends. We weren't sure how he would greet us, so when we managed to find a parking space near his house, I phoned him to say we were passing by and would it be convenient to come in and see him? He was the old Geoff on the phone, surprisingly very friendly, and he seemed pleased that the three of us were there to see him. We didn't feel very friendly towards him, but Julia showed it more than Matt and I put together. Geoff smiled hello to her and she didn't answer him.

Geoff actually asked, 'Why do you look so stern, Julia?' Did he think she still liked him? God knows what planet he was on!

Anyway walking into his lounge the transformation was amazing! Gone were the oversized ornaments, the dark old-fashioned furniture that his mother had loved. The room was completely different. With Scandinavian wood flooring, a plasma-screen television and soft leather furnishings it was minimalist and very tasteful. We thought it looked incredible and I told him so. He seemed pleased that we liked the décor but made no comment on the cost! We sank back into the comfy settees and tried to steer the conversation with a degree of tact towards the difficulties Matt had had to cope with representing himself, until he'd seen a glimmer of hope when Tom Burns had told him what he thought in December 2006. Geoff's corroboration would have meant that Matt would have been freed instantly. We all spoke quietly and looked directly at him, but we never managed eye contact because he kept his head down all the time. He eventually muttered, 'Elliott Taylor is a rat, and I may have heard something!' Bingo! That was enough for Matt. It was all too late to hear this somewhat cryptic answer, which confirmed only what we'd always thought. Matt's patience had finally run out!

His parting words to Deaf Geoff were to do with football, what else? 'If the conversation at Elliott Taylor's chambers on 13th December 2006 had been about your beloved Chelsea and the Premier League, would you have heard what Tom Burns was saying?' The suddenly, not so very deaf Geoff answered Matt's question with a simple yes. As we all walked out he began ranting at us incoherently, but by then we had heard enough. It's sad the way people sell their souls and for what? What did he actually achieve? Very little in our estimation!

A few weeks later we found out by chance that there were so many Matthew Carter deals signed and unsigned flying around the court you could probably use them as wallpaper. The wording was different in every one. So the question was which deal had been placed before Judge Benedict? Which one was the original deal signed by Mr Carter? What did the other deals mean and do we really care? To be perfectly honest, no, not now! We had come to the conclusion long ago that there were too many holes to fill in this case, not least the bugging of my mobile phone, why Deaf Geoff had suddenly developed a hearing problem, how many audio tapes Ben Nicholls had enhanced or deleted, and why had the Inland Revenue kept quiet about their checking up on Mr Carter years before Matt had come on the scene! The list is endless.

I spoke to someone who worked for the House of Commons, who had been informed periodically of Matt's court challenge and final progress. His response was, 'I'm very pleased for him. You shouldn't let them get away with this; many heads should roll!' We totally agree with that comment, but if Matt wanted to take it further, the list of people involved would go on forever! Perhaps Matt will choose a selective few and we'll see what happens! Now that could be a very interesting subject to write about!

I could carry on writing about my husband after his long drawn-out court life finished, but what style would I write it in? The romance genre? Well, he is fairly romantic, but not in the Mills & Boon style! Maybe I should make him a cartoon hero in a children's book and call it *Magician Matt's Magic Morning*? But I can't quite picture that either! So to end this story in an upbeat, positive way, I will remind you that I have let you into our lives to show how desperate measures from the prosecution team opened the judge's eyes and led to a magnificent ruling for Matt Davidson. Too many innocent people are unjustly treated and tagged as guilty simply because the Crown Prosecution Service and the police have been allowed to get away with it for so long! Why do they have the right to do this? The answer to me is very clear: because no one has stopped them! So now is the time for change. None of it is rocket science and you don't have to be a genius to succeed. Just apply good old-fashioned common sense and an unbreakable iron will, and when you know you're in the right, fight! Never give up. It's a great feeling when you win. My husband is a prime example, so what are you waiting for? Go for it!